THE JK

D0552379

Jancis Robinson is superbly qualified to provide a comprehensive, balanced view of alcohol. Her ability to distil the key facts from a bewildering wealth of information, her fresh insights and approach to her chosen subject have brought her international acclaim.

Her *Vines, Grapes and Wines* won major awards on both sides of the Atlantic and has been translated into four languages including French. She passed the notoriously difficult examinations set by the British wine trade to become a Master of Wine at the first attempt, and became British television's first wine personality with her series *The Wine Programme*.

Jancis Robinson is also a journalist with intimate day-to-day knowledge of the drinks industry. She edited the UK trade magazine *Wine & Spirit* for four years, was founder-editor of the *Which? Wine Guide* and in 1980 became Hugh Johnson's distinguished successor as Wine Correspondent of the *Sunday Times*. She writes regular features on wine and food for a wide range of British, American and French publications, and has made many television programmes, including her own series, *Jancis Robinson Meets....*

"The most balanced guide there is to an emotive subject." *Wine*

"Full marks are due for someone who makes her livelihood out of writing about the benefits of alcohol and yet has turned her attention to the cost paid by individuals and society." Anthony Clare, *British Medical Journal*

"Covers nasty aspects ... and jollier ones ... with equal verve, wit and plain good writing." Prue Leith, *Books*

For my friends everywhere, especially those in and around the wine trade, hoping that this book encourages a move towards quality rather than quantity.

Jancis Robinson

THE DEMON DRINK

A User's Guide

Methuen · Mandarin

641.21
/1

A Mandarin Paperback

THE DEMON DRINK

First published in Great Britain 1988
by Mitchell Beazley International Ltd
Artists House, 14–15 Manette Street,
London W1V 5LB
This edition published 1989
by Mandarin Paperbacks
Michelin House, 81 Fulham Road, London SW3 6RB
Mandarin is an imprint of the Octopus Publishing Group
Copyright © Jancis Robinson 1988, 1989

British Cataloguing in Publication Data

Robinson, Jancis
  The demon drink
  1. Alcoholic drinks. Consumption.
  Social aspects.
  I. Title
  306.4

ISBN 0-7493-0014-0

Printed in Great Britain by
Cox & Wyman Ltd, Reading

CONTENTS

PREFACE

Even though wine is my particular passion, when I wrote this book in 1987 I wrote it for the social drinker of any form of alcohol. It was written by and for the intelligent drinker who was concerned about the increasing publicity given to the darker side of drink. I wanted to establish the truth about alcohol, socially as well as medically, and approached my subject with the detachment that seemed both suitable and instinctive for a journalist with some academic training as both a scientist and a philosopher.

I realised I had succeeded in writing a balanced book soon after publication while recording a discussion on alcohol for the World Service with the head of the UK Temperance Alliance and the chief spokesman for the Brewers' Society. Both men took me aside, somewhat conspiratorially, to congratulate me on my assessment of the subject which divides them. It could hardly be that both men agreed with every word I wrote. As was pointed out, however, in the Greater London Alcohol Advisory Service's review of this book, "*The Demon Drink* has been welcomed by both the alcohol industry and the alcohol field. This suggests that perhaps we are all prepared to only take note of the sentences which suit our viewpoint."

This may well be the case. I certainly had the rudest possible illustration of how easy it was, by determinedly selective quotation, to present the book as anti-alcohol propaganda when it was serialised before publication by *The Times*. For all editors, at least during 1988, the agreed line was that Alcohol is Wicked – even when the facts suggest otherwise. An attempt to correct the balance in the *Independent* fared little better. My article attempting to deflate the prevailing moral panic about young people and drink, by sober analysis of the relevant research, was printed as a coda to yet another rather sensational account of the drunken exploits of one or two cooperative "lager louts" (a usefully emotive phrase which was coined in late 1988 and which perhaps symbolises our dangerous objectification of 'the alcohol problem').

As this book shows, there are many reasons why normal middle-aged, middle-class adults deserve to know more about alcohol. There are also many reasons to bless rather than curse alcohol and I see even more need to disseminate and stress these now than I did when I originally wrote the book. The crazier aspects of the anti-alcohol campaign, notably in the United States, have only intensified in the interim. All the more need, therefore, for a truly objective user's guide.

My desire is not to stir up trouble but to take the emotion out of our relationship with alcohol, through genuine knowledge of its place in our bodies and our society.

Jancis Robinson
December 1988

ACKNOWLEDGMENTS

This book could not have been attempted without the encouragement and extensive library of Dr Richard Smith. It would have been considerably worse without the comments of Drs Martin and Moira Plant on the manuscript. The opinions and errors are all mine.

My research was helped most materially and diligently by Lisa Barnard but also by, in alphabetical order, Professor E. A. Barnard, Commander Geoffrey Bond, Naomi Brookes, Linda Barnard Finer, Kenneth Dunjohn, Elizabeth Evans, Gene Ford, Tim Hamilton-Russell, Professor M. H. Kaufman, Margaret Harvey, Dr S. K. Ghosh, Richard Grindal, Roy Johnson, Max Laurie, Catherine Manac'h, Fiona Mulliner, Dr Marsha Morgan, Deborah Moroney, Robin Naughton, Dr Robin Room, Anne Shannon, Don Steele, Olivia Timbs, Anita Wagner, Jeffrey Wormstone, John Witton and Ian M. Young.

CHAPTER ONE

The Darling Demon Drink

Why Write a Book About It?

None of us drinks alcohol. We drink delicious, liberating, inspiring or socially significant liquids which happen to contain alcohol. Yet alcohol is a powerful drug. No matter how many of us see it as a necessary adjunct to our lives, it is abhorred by a high proportion of the world's major religions, and viewed by some as the fount of all evil. How is it that this potentially dangerous substance is so enmeshed in our culture that there are long periods of the week and year when mild intoxication is a majority state for the nation, and teetotallers are regarded as social deviants?

Like more than 85 per cent of British adults, I enjoy drinking. I like the rush of euphoria that the day's first few sips of wine bring. I savour (usually) the nuances of taste and flavour. I like the way that alcohol makes both me and the people I'm with seem more attractive, and the world in general a better place to be. I am also, on the other hand, extremely fond of my health, and feel a particular *tendresse* for my brain and liver. In common with most Britons who read newspapers and watch television, I have become increasingly aware in the last year or two of some rather discomforting and widely disseminated snippets of information about the harm that alcohol can do. It has been extremely difficult, however, to find genuinely objective and comprehensive information aimed at the interested consumer about exactly how much of a demon drink really is.

The scaremongering headlines sit uneasily surrounded by stories one knows have been written by some of the nation's more enthusiastic drinkers, just as many of the headlines have emanated from a profession which has traditionally had one of the highest occupational rates of cirrhosis. There have been few attempts to put the frightening facts into focus, or even to whisper that there may, indeed, be something good to say for the odd drink.

This has been largely because we, the public, have been caught in the crossfire of a debate between a small but vociferous group of campaigners known, even to themselves, as the "anti-alcohol lobby", and government. Perhaps "debate" is still too strong a word for the present level of discourse between these two factions. "Loud heckle" might be a more appropriate description of the lobby's laudable attempts to draw government's attention to the fact that it has been doing so little to tackle society's alcohol-related problems: lost man-hours, violence, accidents, as well as the more medical aspects of alcohol damage.

The most tangible and well-publicized exhibits in the evidence for the prosecution of alcohol in recent years have been the 1986-87 reports of the Royal Colleges of Psychiatrists and Physicians, provocatively entitled *Alcohol: Our Favourite Drug* and *A Great and Growing Evil* respectively, as well as similar reports from the Royal College of General Practitioners and the British Psychological Society.

The anti-alcohol campaigners have been almost goaded into sensationalism by the government's sledgehammer technique of dealing with the abuse of other drugs, heroin in particular. According to Action on Alcohol Abuse, 1986 spending on combatting illegal drugs and solvents worked out at nearly £1 million per user death, whereas the comparable figure for alcohol was just over £100. No wonder those whose job it is to study, on slivers of budgets, the drinking problems of the nation feel entitled to make a fuss.

Nor is it surprising that the campaigners have picked out the most alarming statistics, ripe for tabloid sensationalism, with which to draw attention to the fact that alcohol can damage the nation. Government has been slow to respond, partly of course because alcohol makes such a useful contribution to the Exchequer – a total of more than £4 billion in the year to April 1987, excluding VAT – but perhaps also because it has been the unquestioned inherited wisdom of successive governments that alcohol is a potential vote-loser. Political points are easily lost, the argument goes, fighting the abuse of a majority sport.

I wonder whether that tenet is not due for reappraisal. We are no longer a nation of unthinking drinkers. We enjoy our drink, in an exceptionally liberal social climate compared with our counterparts across the Atlantic and North Sea, but no country that can sustain a book such as Geoffrey Cannon and Caroline Walker's *Food Scandal* for six weeks at the top of the best-seller lists can be said to be apathetic to what it ingests.

We may not have inherited, thank goodness, the prevalent American paranoia about alcohol, that nation's new scapegoat, but we are increasingly becoming a health-conscious nation and showing signs of a similar reassessment of our drinking habits. Lower-alcohol, low-alcohol and no-alcohol drinks proliferate. Our per capita alcohol consumption appears to have peaked. I think many of the country's drinkers are ready for, might even welcome, a comprehensive review of where alcohol sits in our society, and a realistic assessment of its potential harm. The government might even *win* points for initiating a major alcohol education programme.

The government would not necessarily, of course, win points with its allies in the powerful but somewhat ostrich-like drinks industry, with which more than 60 MPs have a direct affiliation. The industry, for all its resources, has been strangely silent throughout the anti-alcohol lobbying. This may be because of disagreement between the various factions – brewers, distillers and wine importers – or simply because those in the drinks trade are the most reluctant to look alcohol, and their own drinking habits in particular, in the eye. The distillers tend to make much of the sums earned by our (or more properly Scotland's) exports of whisky. The brewers prefer to emphasize the number of people they employ (a figure that remains curiously round and constant throughout the years), while the wine importers operate on such low profit margins that most of them can afford only to wince in private. Significantly, and not for the first time in the business of intelligent ingestion – nutritional labelling of food, for example – it was left to one of the supermarkets rather than specialist retailers to lead the way. The first convincing attempt to educate the masses about "sensible drinking" came, in late 1987, in the form of a free, full-colour booklet so entitled from Sainsbury's, now Britain's favourite wine merchant.

The drinks industry is worried, but perhaps more so than it need be. Those who profit from the nation's bibulousness became used to steady growth as Britain recovered its prosperity post-war and have been among the prime beneficiaries of increased consumer spending during Mrs Thatcher's reign. Only its sharpest-witted members are coming to terms with the fact that the British public cannot automatically be expected to go on drinking more and more, and may indeed start to drink a little less. And if drinkers were to pursue quality rather than quantity, the drinks industry could benefit considerably, particularly those prepared to innovate and diversify. We are still going to drink something, and those who will benefit will be those who can provide appetizing (and often highly profitable) low- and non-alcoholic substitutes. It can be easier to make money selling Perrier water than Laurent Perrier champagne.

Continuing a policy first evident in 1979 with the suppression of a "Think Tank" report advising firm action on the social aspects of alcohol, and most dramatically illustrated by the closure of the Health Education Council in 1986 when its director had been too vociferous that too much alcohol was too much, the government has so far done little to encourage those who want to cut down their intake. Until October 1988 full wine duty (73.5p a bottle in 1987) was levied even on wine coolers, which may contain only 2 per cent alcohol; the duty cut-off level of alcohol is an extremely low 1.2 per cent, which means that bottles of low-alcohol wine were until recently no cheaper than bottles of ordinary wine. Slim encouragement to cut down.

The anti-alcohol lobby would be delighted to see duties on all alcoholic drink rise substantially – counter to the principles of the European Community, which would like to see exactly the same duties apply throughout Europe. Harmonization with the almost nonexistent duties on wine in France and Italy and the negligible duties on beer in West Germany is an attractive thought indeed to consumers. But the lobbyists believe that the only way to reduce the harm that alcohol does to society is to make drinking a luxury activity. (They are right to point out that in real terms the price of alcoholic drinks has remained remarkably stable in this country.)

This argument will remind many of the smoking issue, but there are several major differences. The harm done by smoking is almost exclusively medical (the revolting smell apart), whereas excessive drinking can have potentially wider effects. And while even one cigarette does some harm, the point at which alcohol starts to wreak damage is much further up the ladder of consumption. Try as well-funded American researchers might to prove that even moderate consumption of alcohol is a thoroughly bad thing, they have not established any causal relationship between moderate drinking and medical harm. In fact, there is considerable evidence that drinking in moderation is positively beneficial.

I must confess to approaching this thesis with considerable scepticism. Yet well over a score of clinically rigorous studies of different population groups suggest that those who drink moderately are much less likely to suffer coronary heart disease, our biggest killer, than teetotallers. There is also evidence to suggest that a little is better than none in terms of blood pressure – although heavy drinking can raise blood pressure to dangerous levels.

There are several possible explanations for the ability of a controlled dose of alcohol to ward off heart disease, all of them quite technical and some of them quite likely. The most appealing to me is its ability to alleviate stress. Should the medical profession eventually abandon its enquiries into more complicated hypotheses, and decide that alcohol's miracle ingredient is that it can make us relax, this will surely be a vindication of common sense. For most of us know that this is just one of the many good things about alcohol, together with its ability to make us feel sociable, witty, soothed and inspired, in fact to create a world that may be more fantastic than real, but is nevertheless an extremely satisfactory fantasy. There is even some concrete evidence for what I have come to call the "octogenarian vigneron syndrome", the fact that the longevity of many of those who have drunk regularly and enthusiastically throughout their lives is notably high. It is odd that the case for alcohol has been put so rarely, and when it has been, so badly.

In Ignorance Lies Danger

It was partly to provide some of the missing propaganda on the virtues of alcohol that I embarked on this book. It was also, and more importantly, to try to examine dispassionately, in context, the medical evidence for and against drinking. After all, I have been drinking regularly for nearly 20 years, and almost every day for the last 12 years. I wanted to find out the facts, as I imagine many intelligent drinkers would, for the most selfish of reasons.

I would love to be able to report to my fellow wine enthusiasts and other keen drinkers at this point: "All clear, folks. Dangers wildly overstated. Carry on boozing." But I'm afraid I can't. The case against alcohol as it has reached the public *has* been overstated, but not wildly so.

The most sensational aspects of alcohol damage – brain atrophy and shrinkage of sexual organs being surely the most arresting – are found only in severe alcohol abusers. There is really no justification for headlines of the "Drink'll Wrinkle Your Winkle" genre. Fewer than ten of the 42 entries in the *Summary of physical health hazards associated with alcohol abuse* drawn up by the Royal College of Physicians apply to anyone other than those who drink extremely heavily indeed. But examination of the evidence suggests all too clearly that alcohol *is* responsible for considerable medical damage, with the liver being in the front line for most of us. The range of ill-effects examined in Chapter Five shows that much of the damage is not necessarily fatal, but could well contribute to the worsening of other conditions and to a deterioration of health in general.

Perhaps the most important aspect of the more medical passages of this book, however, is the identification of certain groups of people who are particularly vulnerable to certain forms of alcoholic ravage, even at quite low levels of consumption (see Chapters Seven and Eight). It makes sense for anyone who drinks regularly to find out whether they belong to a high-risk group and, even if they do not, to learn the practical ways in which the damage inflicted by alcohol can be minimized.

Probably my most devastating single discovery is just how and why women are so much more vulnerable than men to alcohol damage, and how much less likely we are to recover from it. I also uncovered a particularly horrifying statistic, surprisingly underplayed to date. Whereas in almost every other country in which such records are kept the rate of cirrhosis mortality among women is only half, and sometimes only a tenth, of the cirrhosis mortality rate of men, in Britain women are very nearly as likely as men to die of this incurable liver disease. Do British women drink that much more than their counterparts elsewhere?

The adverse effects of occasional drinking during pregnancy have almost certainly been exaggerated, particularly in the United States, but another revelation to me, publicly underreported, is the extent to which drinking in men, as well as women, can affect fertility. Better dissemination of this information could save considerable anxiety, time and expense.

Also important is the fact that alcohol reacts with all sorts of medication and medical conditions. Since drinking (and pill-taking) is such a common activity, intelligent drinkers would do well to inform themselves on the interactions and increased risks outlined in Chapter Eight.

I can see how the doctors arrived at their, to some impossibly stringent, "safe levels" – an average of three modest drinks, or "units", of alcohol a day for men and two for women. But I can also see how bland and generalized that picture is. Some people can undoubtedly drink considerably more than this without damage, but for others even these amounts may be too generous.

Every intelligent drinker owes it to his (and, particularly, her) liver, and gut, and brain, and children, to find out more about alcohol and about whether they fall into any of the particularly high-risk groups, which include such disparate categories as those with a small frame, an ulcer, high blood pressure, or a job on a boat. As a woman whose work takes her perilously close to two high-risk occupations, the drinks trade and writers, I now realize somewhat reluctantly that I have to watch my own intake.

But it is not enough simply to know what the risks are. Every responsible drinker needs to know exactly, and very practically, how to minimize them, to understand fully, for example, how sensible is the advice always to eat when drinking, never to quench thirst with alcoholic drinks, and to be able to detect the first signs of dependence on alcohol.

Perhaps the most important single aspect of informing ourselves about alcohol is finding out exactly how much alcohol there is in each measure of each sort of drink. It seems ludicrous that we have had to wait until May 1988 for legislation that compels those who sell alcoholic drinks to let us in on the secret, in an easily intelligible way. Some of those who argued against this suggested such information should be kept from the public because we would automatically head for the most alcoholic options. I think there is much more to be lost by letting people take strong drinks without knowing it. How many people realize, for example, that Carlsberg Special is nearly three times as strong as some standard beers and as strong, sip for sip, as some wines? Or that an Amarone from Italy, or some of California's ripest wines, can be nearly as strong as Bailey's Irish Cream? Or that Pernod is almost twice as strong as Campari? In ignorance lies danger.

Now, at last, all drinks should be labelled with their alcoholic content in terms of the percentage of the volume taken up by alcohol. Thus, spirits-based drinks are usually 18-40 per cent, wines 8-18 per cent, beers 3-12 per cent. Chapter Seven, What Is a Drink, Anyway? and Chapter Eight, Choosing, or What (and How) to Drink, point out clearly how much of what sort of drink represents the medical profession's "unit" of alcohol.

Another blow has been to find that in the official literature the doctors have been painting rather too rosy a picture of how much wine we can safely drink. Their "unit" of alcohol was chosen as eight grams because it most closely approximates to half a pint of ordinary lager or bitter or a single pub measure (if the pub is in England and not Scotland or Ireland) of spirits such as gin, whisky and brandy. This they blithely translate into "a glass" of wine. True of the average-strength wine at 12 per cent, sadly, only if you pour nine glasses to the bottle, or eight glasses of 11 per cent wine. You *can* get more than 20 glasses from a bottle at a cerebral wine tasting, but at most dining tables I know the average glass, or what we regard as "a glass", holds a sixth of a bottle.

We need to see the medical evidence in perspective, however. As a Professor of Psychiatry at the University of Edinburgh admitted at an important lecture in 1987 called *Drinking Sensibly*, moderate alcohol consumption is certainly safer than cycling to work. Alcohol is not a major killer. It may, as sensationally reported on BBC's *Panorama* programme in October 1987, kill more people than heroin, but then the number of heroin users is a tiny fraction of the 40 million people who drink alcohol. Whereas heart disease (to which *heavy* drinkers are admittedly more prone) and cancer between them killed more than 400,000 Britons in 1985, the number of known deaths from cirrhosis (by no means all of which were alcohol related) was just over 2,500, with another 1,000-1,500 killed in accidents in which alcohol was involved.

The difficulty in arriving at a true numerical picture of alcohol casualties, however, has given rise to one of the issues most hotly debated among the many warring factions in the anti-alcohol lobby. Estimates vary, and once even reached the 40,000 total wildly cited by the Royal College of General Practitioners in their 1986 report, more soberly entitled *Alcohol – A Balanced View*. Alcohol is almost certainly a *factor* in thousands more deaths than those officially noted as alcohol related, but doctors in England and Wales (less so in Scotland) have traditionally been too polite to note it on innumerable death certificates. Perhaps partly as part of a national conspiracy to ignore our most widespread drug problem, society in general and the medical profession in particular have contrived to overlook the fact that our favourite drug has some perceptible ill-effects.

Mirroring government's traditional apathy towards alcohol-related problems is a national dearth of statistics on them. There is not even any national reporting by hospitals or emergency departments of the number of accidents or crimes involving alcohol, and only a proportion of general practitioners collect information on the extent to which alcohol affects their patients. These worrying lacunae help to explain why it has taken us so long to face the less attractive side of alcohol.

What Can Be Done?

While looking carefully at the facts about drinking, I have been struck by the extent to which they are at odds with drinking lore. Gout is *not* caused by alcohol. There is no scientific basis for believing that mixing different drinks has any worse effect on us than, for example, drinking exclusively the products of grape or of grain. Drinking neat spirits is *not* the fastest way of getting alcohol into the system, although there is an argument that alcohol abuse as an issue was born when alcohol was first distilled and available in such a concentrated form. We owe the art of distillation and the word alcohol itself to the Arabs, who were sufficiently wary of their discovery to forswear it.

There is no cure for a hangover other than time, and a bit of prophylactic nonalcoholic drinking. Beer is slightly better nutritionally than wine, but in terms of overall medical effect, no form of alcohol is better than another (although anything that encourages us to eat while we drink, such as wine, is to be admired). The Scots are *not* great drinkers, consuming below the national average per head, although Scottish – and Welsh – drinkers do tend to concentrate their intake on the weekend more than their English counterparts, possibly to their livers' relief. In fact, Scotland is more enlightened than England and Wales in recognizing and treating alcohol problems.

The British in general are not among the world's most enthusiastic drinkers, and we have in the past drunk much more beer and spirits than we do today. But our total per capita intake of all forms of alcohol is now more than half that in the world's most bibulous nations, France and Portugal. We consume rather less per head than similar cultures in the old colonies, the United States, Australia and New Zealand, which is ironic in view of the fact that we, like the French and Spaniards, so shamelessly used alcohol as a weapon of colonization and tool of trade, particularly the slave trade. We also smiled upon alien drugs such as opium and cannabis when it suited us for our Far Eastern interests.

Indeed, the history and geography of attitudes to various drugs around the world is a fascinating reflection of expediency, self-delusion and self-interest. Alcohol happens to be so widely acceptable because it is historically Europe's favourite drug and so much of the world is dominated by European culture. We are sometimes irrationally alarmed by alien drugs, particularly the relatively innocuous cannabis, simply because they are unfamiliar. Man seems to need some form of mind-altering substance as an escape route or life enhancer, but many of us continue to pretend that we treasure alcohol for other properties.

The typical Briton does not like to feel that he is not fully in control, that there could be a substance he ingests frequently that has any power over him. We are mysteriously coy about our drinking and its consequences. Just think how rarely we admit to being or having been inebriated, even when we have drunk quite enough to put our blood-alcohol levels well over the legal limit for driving. Is this because we, like the Swedes and Americans, feel guilty about our drinking? Geographical comparison of attitudes to alcohol suggests that predominantly Protestant cultures feel much the same set of guilts about drink as Roman Catholics are brought up to feel about sex.

Like the average Frenchman, I see no reason to associate guilt with drinking. Alcohol is one of life's great gifts. Provided we know how to use it, it can enrich our lives enormously. We would all be in a better position to understand and therefore control our drinking if we were more honest about it, and more positively assented to its beneficial mind-changing effects. We should both enjoy and monitor our alcoholic intake, but we can do that only if we face up to it.

Perhaps we even need to take the steam out of the word drug, and see all the potent substances we ingest as a group ranged along a scale of potential harm. On that basis, alcohol would unquestionably deserve a lower noxiousness rating than heroin or cocaine, but would warrant a higher one than either caffeine (which nevertheless probably has a higher dependency potential than alcohol) or the illegal drug cannabis.

There are a number of very simple steps we could take to improve our relationship with alcohol, apart from becoming much more aware of the substance itself. Those outlined in Chapter Eight are mainly personal, such as working out how much alcohol is in our customary glass, or always providing a nonalcoholic alternative, or getting out of the habit of forcing drinks on others.

Other valuable reforms would be less domestic. In Britain we are still shamefully underdeveloped in our sense of responsibility over drunken driving (unlike the Scandinavians). We need to face up much more squarely to the sometimes fatal consequences of taking to the wheel under the influence of alcohol, which perniciously deludes us into a false sense of self-confidence. As a society we have not yet fully acknowledged the implications of combining two such potent forces as alcohol and the motor car, and it may well take random breath testing to force us to do so. The civil liberties arguments against random testing seem extremely weak, for the police already have the power to stop a wide range of drivers. And each year the public majority in favour increases, almost as though we ourselves recognize the need for this external straitjacket on our anti-social behaviour. It can be only on economic grounds that the government can defend its torpidity on this issue, but random breath testing would surely cost but a fraction of the several billion pounds which our drinking deflects into the Treasury each year.

There is also a pressing need for better alcohol education for the young, although no method has as yet proved demonstrably successful. It may be that youthful exuberance is by its nature untamable, and that alcohol, one of several powerful novelties of the teens, will always be one of the ways in which that exuberance is expressed. Heavier penalties for young drunken drivers or lower blood-alcohol limits are possible ways of lessening the impact. Alcohol restrictions are playing a major part in the fight against football and other hooliganism, but this can only have the effect of adding dangerously to the symbolic value of alcohol among the young. The most salutory example of how effectively this forbidden-fruit principle works was the "noble experiment" of Prohibition in the United States, which was followed by one of the worst periods of mass alcoholic excess that the world has known.

The anti-alcohol lobby sees that the nation would be richer and healthier if we all drank a bit less, and is accordingly campaigning for higher drinks prices through taxation. I would much rather this were achieved by our own volition: mature action based on a sense of responsibility. But there are other external ways of manipulating our alcohol intake.

During World War I, Lloyd George managed to reduce considerably the strength of beer and spirits. Spirits are in any case diluted, "broken down", to the accepted strengths at which they are currently sold, so one profitable line of enquiry for researchers in the gin and whisky industries would be to pursue how to maintain the quality of their products at slightly lower, healthier strengths. Likewise with beer. The average strength of the produce of Britain's breweries declined from 5.5 per cent at the turn of the century to 3.8 per cent by 1986 – although this average is rising again, due chiefly to the increased popularity of high-strength lagers. The brewers and distillers could respond even more energetically to the demands of a more health-conscious market, as could the vintners.

In most years a high proportion of the wines produced in northern Europe have their alcoholic strength raised by a century-old technique called chaptalization: adding fermentable sugar to the grape juice and fermenting it out to alcohol, together with the natural grape sugar. This seems an odd practice in these late 1980s when even the French and Italians are trying to cut down their alcohol intake. The argument is that chaptalization evens out the variation in grape ripeness in different years and that unchaptalized wines taste unattractively puny, but we could presumably accustom ourselves to them if sufficiently motivated. If winemakers can now produce no-alcohol and low-alcohol wines, they could surely experiment with increasing the quality of unchaptalized wines.

We in Britain are at a challenging geographical and historical cross-roads in our relationship with strong drink. We can choose from a wider range of libations than any other nation. We have given the world two of its most widely appreciated spirits, gin and Scotch whisky. Our ancestors were responsible for the creation of the world's greatest fortified wines: sherry, port and madeira. Today, London could fairly be said to be the fine-wine capital of the world, thanks to its auction houses and its concentration of non-chauvinistic connoisseurship.

We are free of the constricting social stigma that attaches to drinking in much of Scandinavia and America, where even wine duty is happily referred to as a "sin tax". We share our Mediterranean counterparts' insouciance about drink, but we are much better informed than most of them about the potential dangers of alcohol misuse. We no longer have any excuse to keep on toping in ignorance, waiting for excess to make itself known to us through our livers.

We now have sufficient evidence on which to base a more mature stage in our relationship with alcohol: one in which we can recognize fully and in much more precise detail the dangers associated with it but also, gloriously and unashamedly, its unique contribution to life. The art of intelligent drinking is to know how much is enough, occasionally to drink more than that, sometimes nothing at all, and to savour every delicious drop.

CHAPTER TWO

Alcohol Can Be Good

For You

The Missing Message

On October 22, 1986, at the Guildhall in London, Anthony Thwaite announced the winner of that year's Booker Prize to 600,000 television viewers and to the 200 assembled literati who were sipping either Hine vsop or armagnac, having already enjoyed champagne, Chablis 1985, Château Lalande-Borie 1981 and a rather superior Muscat de Beaumes-de-Venise.

The popular winner was Kingsley Amis for his book *The Old Devils*, about a group of ill-fulfilled Welshmen whose most notable remaining prowess was in raising glasses to their lips. He rose to his feet, tried to look surprised, managed to look delighted, and announced that he planned to spend most of the £15,000 prize money on whisky. Few in the room questioned his wisdom, and not just because of the customary post-prandial glow. The relationship between alcohol and artistic creativity is as long-established as it has been carefully nurtured. Kingsley Amis just happens to be one current novelist who has most vividly and memorably invited the drinks, drunks and drinkers in his life on to the printed page.

Most writing about the effects of alcohol – both in fiction and in its antithesis, medical literature – concentrates on drinking in excess or in extremis. Remarkably little is written or, in my experience, voiced either publicly or in conversation about the sheer pleasure of a much more sensible, and much more usual, intake of alcohol. It is as though there were a tacit social agreement, just as there was about sex a century ago, not to discuss this very private pleasure. Indeed, it may well be another set of guilts, late-twentieth century this time, that makes so many of us reluctant to confront our drinking habits and responses to alcohol. Most of us say we drink because we like the taste, or we find it relaxing, or to be sociable. Few of us are prepared to admit that we might ever treasure alcohol for its psychoactive properties, its ability to alter our mental state.

The precise physical effects of strong drink on the body are examined in Chapter Five, but these details merely fill in the scientific background to what most people – and certainly most people who will have picked up this book – already know to be a most agreeable sensation (however inevitably they associate it with guilt). A single drink taken fast can induce a rush of euphoria. One sipped with more decorum brings on a more measured state of wellbeing, of relaxation, a feeling that the body is not a frazzle of nerve ends but is being oiled by some particularly soothing unguent. Other people suddenly seem more attractive, the world a better place to be; desires seem more desirable, problems less problematical. And, *provided* intake and frequency are kept at that elusive level that passes muster as "moderate", these effects are probably entirely beneficial.

How fortunate we are to have recourse to a lifter of the spirits that in most societies is legally condoned, not difficult to find, in many forms not expensive to buy and which, if consumed sensibly, draws man closer to fellow man, providing at least short-term relief from his problems. The Royal College of Psychiatrists in its 1986 report, so challengingly entitled *Alcohol: Our Favourite Drug*, seems to view this phenomenon rather snootily: "After a few drinks conversation appears to sparkle, dull people seem more interesting and feeble jokes funny." But how much better and restorative in many circumstances a mild and exhilarating fantasy can be than a remorselessly clenched grasp on what is often grim reality. Party games can be an important and valuable part of life.

But there should be no doubt about it. Alcohol *is* a psychoactive substance, even though remarkably few members of Westernized twentieth-century cultures are willing to recognize the fact, or its benefits. We shy away from admitting to its regular use for its mind-altering properties – not just because of unwelcome connotations with the LSD of the sixties, the dope of the seventies and the heroin of the eighties but also, I suspect, because we like to persuade ourselves, despite any amount of evidence to the contrary, that we are always in control. Perhaps if we could relax and admit the whole truth about alcohol (and not just claim to drink it for its effect on our social lives, our sleeping patterns or our dinner tables), we could also be more honest about our drinking habits and better able to analyse and control them.

This plea for the social benefits to the individual of moderate alcohol consumption (quite apart from the claims to medical benefits discussed later in this chapter) is difficult to make in the current climate of opinion about drink and drinking. The demon drink, long accepted as an inevitable feature in the backdrop of Western life, has in the last few years been marched firmly towards centre stage for a more thorough inspection – not often enough by consumers but by a relatively small, voluble group in and around the medical profession who have noticed, quite rightly, that it is alcohol's turn for the limelight.

Those whose livelihood depends on selling alcoholic drinks have reacted in some cases with predictable paranoia and occasional overstatement. Some American wine producers and the US liquor trade talk of neo-Prohibitionists, while their UK counterparts purse their lips over the "anti-alcohol lobby". It is facile to argue, as some elements in the British drinks trade do, that these are campaigners who fought and won the battle for more controls on nicotine and simply need another cause. Many of them are acting from the noblest of motives. Dr Richard Smith, for instance, an unexpectedly hedonistic campaigner against alcohol abuse, admits in no less weighty a publication than the *British Medical Journal* (of which he is deputy editor) in an article entitled *Preventing Alcohol Problems: A Job for Canute?*: "To most of us life without alcohol is unimaginable". He will also admit, with refreshing realism, that his worst hangovers have been visited on him at international conferences on alcoholism.

These toilers over the problems of alcohol abuse are not necessarily anti-alcohol but they *are* pro-temperance, meaning the opposite of intemperance rather than complete abstention. They might be called the new temperance reformers.

They work in the shadow of a particularly portentous curve. The work of a French mathematical theoretician, Sully Ledermann, in the 1950s, it makes the unwelcome assertion that the higher the average consumption of alcohol in a given society, the greater the number of people who are seriously damaged by alcohol. The curve, and independent statistical analyses since, show that in homogenous societies the higher the peak of average consumption, the longer the downhill curve on the right is forced to slide over people who are drinking far more than is good for them. Total national alcohol

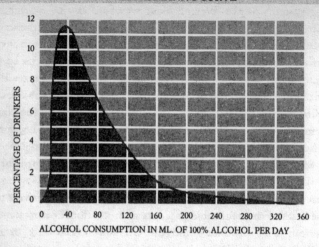

ALCOHOL CONSUMPTION IN ML. OF 100% ALCOHOL PER DAY

consumption may seem of little personal relevance. To the average health-conscious drinker, patterns of acceptable behaviour inside the steep, normal bulge of the curve are much more important than the excesses at the far right-hand end. But although the curve is simplistic, it is widely accepted as sad but true that a society can limit the extent to which it is damaged only by restraining per capita consumption.

In the last 100 years, for instance, comparison of average alcohol consumption per head in the UK with the number of death certificates signed as a result of cirrhosis, delirium tremens or chronic alcoholism shows a depressing correlation. What might be called "drunken deaths" accounted for one in under 5,000 people at the turn of the century (low relative to other causes of death), just after Britain's drinking reached its last major peak since its stupefying all-time high, not, surprisingly enough, in Gin Lane days but in the supposedly prim and proper 1870s. Towards the end of the 1970s, as consumption started to approach turn-of-the-century levels, it was inevitable and right that this fact would be trumpeted.

Even though the evils of drink have perhaps been trumpeted at a slightly exaggerated volume, and we take our alcohol now in quite different forms and social settings, Fleet Street and television journalists have been easy targets for the carefully prepared and alarming statistics lobbed at them by the new reformers. Those in the media have, of course, concentrated on the more sensational aspects. "Drink'll Wrinkle Your Winkle – Official" headlined the *Sun* (April 3, 1987) in a typical response to the sexy bits of recent medical reports on alcohol by tabloid sub-editors, a group not exactly noted· for abstemiousness themselves. In the welter of scare stories, and the unexpectedly dramatic shrinkage in 1986 of what the medical profession decreed were "safe limits", those who might have extolled the pleasures of occasional and moderate drinking went into retreat, many of them settling down to pass the port and platitudes to each other around the drinks trade's more hospitable boardroom tables.

In the United States, the case against alcohol has been promulgated vociferously for more than a century, but the climate of opinion against drinking in any form is even tougher now, and few dare to even whisper the other side of the argument. Gene Ford, a loner in the Pacific Northwest, left the drinks trade to do just that. He launched his *Moderate Drinking Journal* at the beginning of 1987, and in eight months had enticed no more than 100 subscribers. The California wine newspaper *The Wine Spectator* quoted his complaint that: "Those who work in the alcoholic beverage industry are woefully uninformed about the physiological effects of the products they sell ... There are 200 pieces of anti-alcohol legislation in all 50 states right now. And the industry's not fighting back."

Perhaps there are very personal reasons why those of us who work in and around the drinks industry have been so unwilling to immerse ourselves in the details of, for instance, cirrhosis. The industry may suspect the facts are more fundamentally alarming than they are, which is why it has rarely dared to equip itself sufficiently to disseminate the message in favour of moderate consumption – a curious and somewhat sinister lacuna.

Those few who have been prepared to put their heads up from behind the parapet and wave a flag for the odd glass or two have been rewarded by resounding cheers by the normally silent drinking majority. The *Reader's Digest*'s most requested reprint, for example, was reportedly of an article promulgating "the Mediterranean Diet". The wine prescribed by the "diet" was generally thought to be a more alluring constituent than the garlic.

In 1974 a French doctor, Dr E. A. Maury, had published a book, *Soignez-vous par le Vin*, in which he prescribed a different wine for every current and most conceivable ailments – in rather more robust quantities than those to be laid down 12 years later as a safe maximum by the Royal Colleges in London. An English-language version, entitled perhaps inevitably *Wine* –

The Best Medicine, was received with equal enthusiasm. As one of New York's canniest publishers remarked wistfully in the eighties, any book called "Drink Your Way to Health with Five Martinis a Day" would sell a million. The audience is there, but no one is preaching to them.

What is needed, of course, is something far from such a dangerously extremist message. So that we can enjoy and control our drinking by lifting the shroud of guilt that is settling on it more comfortably by the day, it needs to be stressed that alcohol is not like nicotine. One cigarette a day is bad for the health of the smoker and those he or she lives with. One drink a day is not, counter to the impression given by careless reporting of statistical correlationships such as that between alcohol consumption and breast cancer. There is no convincing evidence that moderate drinking is in itself a bad thing – and there is even some carefully nurtured evidence to the contrary. (The crucial questions of how to define "moderate drinking", and how to stick to it, are discussed in Chapters Seven and Eight.)

The most heartening – a particularly appropriate adjective – medical evidence in favour of moderate alcohol consumption emerged from more than a score of different studies in various countries throughout the seventies. Nearest home was one published in *The Lancet* in 1981, the result of a ten-year study of more than 18,000 male civil servants in Whitehall.

A J-shaped curve demonstrated neatly that those who drank a little were less likely than those who abstained completely to die from a heart attack. Those who drank more than two drinks a day forfeited their claim to this indulgence on the part of the Grim Reaper, according to this study – although the rate of coronary heart disease in the French, who drink exceptionally valiant quantities of wine, is notably low. Other studies, including a ten-year survey of 85,000 people in Oakland, California, corroborate a link between moderate drinking and low incidence of heart attacks. The initial theory that this had something to do with alcohol's effect on cholesterol levels has now been widely abandoned, and a substitute explanation is proving elusive. There may, of course, be no causal link, simply a statistical connection.

A similar correlation has been demonstrated between alcohol consumption and raised blood pressure – and therefore hypertension, and therefore strokes. The "J" shape is much less pronounced on plots correlating alcohol consumption and raised blood pressure – although the report of the Royal College of Physicians on alcohol, *A Great and Growing Evil*, published in April 1987, did concede that "people who drink no more than 20g alcohol, who limit themselves to two standard drinks, daily have slightly lower blood pressures than teetotallers."

This was good news indeed for moderate drinkers (and all those who optimistically thought of themselves as such) because of the high incidence of heart attacks and strokes. Cardiovascular diseases are by far the most common cause of premature death, more common than all other causes put together (and more than 100 times more common than the combined total of the diseases most closely associated with alcohol: cirrhosis and chronic liver disease). These findings have been reported with glee in publications concerned with the drinks trade and the more stimulating forms of gastronomy, and continue to be trotted out for display whenever convenient.

It must be said, however, that the vital little left-hand upswing of these "J"s may be very brittle indeed. The campaigners argue that those at the left-hand, zero extremity of any plot of alcohol consumption, the teetotallers or "abstainers", may be a funny, unrepresentative bunch; that they may forswear alcohol because of their own inherent weakness or ill-health; that in some surveys the group of abstainers may well include reformed alcohol abusers, in whom some of the damage found further along the curve has already been done.

Hardline evidence that moderate alcohol consumption can stave off any other medical complaints is thin on the ground, although no one who visits the traditional wine-producing regions of the world can fail to be impressed by the conjunction of longevity and capacity so happily apparent in its inhabitants. It is hardly surprising that the world's major wine producers, France and Italy, have been slow to respond to the message of health through moderation, and are many years behind the US and UK in research on some of the socio-medical aspects of drinking. Had they been quicker off the mark, there might already be to hand some quantification of the rosy-cheeked octogenarian vigneron syndrome, on which little has been added to a paper written by R. Pearl and published by Alfred Knopf of New York as long ago as 1926 on *Alcohol and Longevity*.

What the pro-drink faction does have at its disposal is a study conducted in 1960 at the Cushing hospital for the elderly near Boston, Massachusetts. (Two decades of "neo-prohibitionism" later, funding for such a study might have been harder to come by.) The study provides scientific evidence for some of alcohol's most widely perceived benefits: as a pick-me-up and – subsequently, presumably – a sedative. Six afternoons a week, a cocktail hour was instituted during which the patients were administered beer, cheese and biscuits. Within two months, the percentage of patients needing sedation dropped from 75 to zero, the percentage that could be described as actively mobile zoomed up from 21 to 75 and, rather more mysteriously, there was a correspondingly dramatic drop in male incontinence.

Alcohol as a sedative is perhaps the form in which it is most commonly known. We give and are given it from the gripewater stage (the leading British brand, billed as "Important To Mothers", is currently 4.4% alcohol, about the same as beer), through the calming drop of brandy so widely prescribed during adult life, to palliative nightcaps for the elderly.

Some surprisingly eminent members of the medical profession have pointed out the saving to the nation if some of those who regularly take sleeping pills, tranquillizers and sedatives could be relied on to administer their own moderate drops and drams of a less pharmaceutical nature. A high proportion of the population has indubitably been doing so for years in any case, whether they admit it to themselves or not.

Alcohol was almost certainly man's first analgesic. As a painkiller and, indeed, antiseptic (as in the oft-quoted: "Take a little wine for thy stomach's sake"), the efficacy of alcohol has long been noted. It was at one time commonly administered by the medical profession as an anaesthetic, and there are still doctors in Britain who prescribe milk stout to nursing mothers. Their American counterparts wouldn't dare.

It is not hard to see how ethyl alcohol in any form could make someone *feel* healthier. It takes a dogged or highly motivated scientist to provide concrete evidence that alcohol can actually *be* healthier. Motivation took a firm grip on Dr Janet McDonald, a San Franciscan nutritionist and public-affairs specialist for her aptly named employers, the Food and Drug Administration, at a symposium on Wine, Health and Society convened by the California Wine Institute in Washington DC in February 1986.

The papers were carefully screened for their pro-wine content, of course. But Dr McDonald presented the results of a study at the University of California, Berkeley, which demonstrated that wine contains elements that significantly encourage the absorption of such useful minerals as calcium, phosphorus, magnesium and zinc from foods eaten with it. She also reported on a study in South Africa (where wine production is as important as in California, and considerably more white wine is produced than red) which showed that white wine helped the absorption of iron. Thus, drinking wine with meals, a practice which anyone who takes the slightest notice of their taste buds knows to be a source of enormous sensory and intellectual pleasure, can – phew! – be justified at least in part on nutritional grounds. (This is not of any great help to those in the distilled spirits industry. Controls using pure ethanol instead of wine showed no improvement in mineral absorption, but it probably won't stop them slipping it in to bulk out a pro-alcohol booklet or two.)

Some of the most optimistic treatises have tried to argue that wine, with its sugars and traces of vitamins and minerals (so capitalized on by Dr Maury who, for example, prescribed Graves, slightly higher in iron than most wines, as a cure for anaemia), is a food in itself. It is true that wine has, in its time, been used simply as fuel: the daily litre of strong red wine that was at one time the norm in Mediterranean farming communities provided, after all, about 1,000 calories, or almost a third of an active man's daily requirements. But taken at much lower, safer levels, wine cannot offer significant amounts of vitamins or minerals. Its carbohydrate content from the alcohol and, in some cases, sugar it contains should not be overlooked by slimmers or diabetics – although dry wines, and diluted spirits, have been recommended in the treatment of diabetes because alcohol is metabolized without needing insulin, nor does it cause insulin secretion.

An average glass of wine, red or white, contains 15 per cent of a man's daily recommended intake of iron and ten per cent of a woman's, but otherwise beers have rather more to offer the body in the form of nutrition. A half pint contains seven per cent of the recommended daily allowances of riboflavin, 13 per cent of niacin, 11 per cent of pyridoxine and five per cent of folacin. There is evidence that some of the least-industrially produced beers, notably in Africa, may make a real contribution to health, notably as sources of protein and B vitamins.

Spirits have even less to offer nutritionally and their higher alcohol levels bring correspondingly more calories, not to mention those in the mixers with which they are so commonly diluted. (See page 90.)

No, strong drink as nourishment is an attractive theory which must be ruled out, although many would attest to wine's efficacy as a stimulant to appetite and an aid to digestion.

No survey of the pleasures and benefits of drink would be complete without taking note of the more cerebral aspects of connoisseurship. It is hard to believe that the activities of wine fanatics, real-ale enthusiasts and lovers of fine whiskies and brandies are but a cover for getting drunk. Do scores of new wine books appear each year simply to prop up the illusion that wine drinkers still have brain cells? Has CAMRA's energetic campaign for real ale in place of big-business beer been simply to smooth its members' path to oblivion? Is the painstaking cask selection and bottling of individual malt whiskies by the Scotch Malt Whisky Society simply a genteel front for inebriation?

Of course not. Wine, beer and whisky fanatics are as boringly intrigued by the minutiae of their fanaticisms as their counterparts who collect stamps and make model aeroplanes. What really enthuses them is not the prospect of a fifth glass but another five minutes' discussion on the provenance of the wood in which it was matured. In fact, to many the alcohol content of the objects of connoisseurship is a positive hindrance. As someone who should regularly taste more than 30 different wines in a day *and* write about them afterwards, I can't wait for an anti-intoxicant to come on the market (see Chapter Five, A Tantalizing Discovery).

One measure of how circumspectly the business of sampling the liquids themselves is viewed is that it is carefully referred to as tasting rather than drinking. The wine enthusiast spits out when tasting in non-social circumstances, and spirits are merely "nosed", thereby minimizing the amount of alcohol entering the system. In my own experience, the alcohol content of wines – far from providing the motive – is one of the few inconveniences of wine as a subject for study. Physical fatigue under the onslaught of alcohol, even the small amount ingested by those of us who try to expectorate every mouthful (however disgusting this might look), often prevents me from fully satisfying my intellectual curiosity about a range of wines – and I deeply resent it.

Those professionals who specialize in studying attitudes to alcohol would doubtless view this with some scepticism, and there is a certain amount of evidence to suggest they are right to do so. Martin Plant, one of Britain's most energetic researchers into alcohol and society, has subjected those who work in the drinks trade to rigorous scrutiny. His object was to establish whether the relatively high incidence of cirrhosis among those employed in trades allied to drinks and drinking was because keen drinkers deliberately chose such careers, or whether the nature of the jobs tended to increase consumption. He found that both were the case: that people entering the drinks trade tend to be heavier-than-average drinkers, and are encouraged within the trade to become even heavier drinkers.

While there is at least half a world of difference between those who apply for jobs on a whisky bottling line and those who decide, as true amateurs, that, say, wine is the one thing that fascinates them most, it is reasonable to suppose that members of the second group are unlikely to hate drinking. For some people there is perhaps an element of sanctioning a potentially dangerous habit by surrounding it with the trappings of connoisseurship, but those trappings are surely too cumbersome to provide the whole explanation.

No one who has ever read a wine magazine can deny that such connoisseurship can provide hours of pleasure in which the actual consumption of alcohol hardly plays a part. Quite apart from the endless talk, the subjects as diverse as history, geography, botany, physics, chemistry, meteorology and psychology that wine, at least, can entail, there is the very real gastronomic pleasure of drinking at the table – as well, of course, as the sheer deliciousness of good wine.

It is not only medically sensible to eat and drink concurrently, to slow the rate of absorption of alcohol into the system. It is also a practice that, without being the slightest pretentious, can transform a daily routine into a positive pleasure. We all have to eat, and as long as the forces of civilization triumph over the desire of scientists to impose evidence of their technological breakthroughs on us, we will continue to make a ritual of it rather than simply popping a nourishing pill. This means that mealtimes will continue to present one of the few focuses of family life and a major catalyst for interaction in a wider social sense. There thus seems every reason to maximize the pleasure that mealtimes can provide.

When it comes down to it, however, most drinks that could contribute anything to a gastronomic partnership contain either sugar or a potentially harmful drug. With the noble exception of water, an excellent, health-giving but essentially vapid thirst quencher, most alcohol-free drinks are either too sweet to complement savoury food or, in the case of tea and coffee, contain that other psychoactive drug, caffeine. The sugars in most wines, beers and spirits have been fermented into alcohol. The drinks themselves are, in the sweetness sense at least, dry, and many of them provide a perfect foil for a wide range of different foods.

At first glance it may appear odd that such a high proportion of foods of European origin, such as so many North American ones, are designed to be enhanced by alcoholic drinks. Looked at in a historical perspective, however, it is hardly surprising that a culture in which alcohol is so firmly embedded should have developed a cuisine that embraces alcoholic drinks so firmly.

The converse is also true, of course. The reason so many gastronomically sensitive palates forgo their customary glass of wine with Chinese food, favouring jasmine tea instead, is that the vine never took firm cultural root in China. This by no means implies that the Chinese are without their problems of alcohol abuse. It simply means that their society is denied one of the Western world's greatest sensual (and social) pleasures: matching food and wine.

While it is true that the problems associated with alcohol tend to be largely social rather than medical (in contrast to those associated with nicotine), it is also true that one of the great boons of moderate drinking has to be measured in social terms. Alcohol: the perfect mixer.

There are those who argue in favour of alcohol on more macro-social grounds. The argument goes that, in Britain alone, for example, approximately three-quarters of a million people are in employment associated with the drinks trade. This figure, trotted out by industry spokesmen each time the Chancellor of the Exchequer works out whether to raise excise duties, should be taken as a generous guestimate. It includes not only those directly involved in the country's distilleries, breweries and drinks bottlers (some of the country's less labour-intensive businesses) but also all those employed in selling domestic and imported drinks at wholesale and retail levels, in shops, pubs and the catering trade. The drinks trade in various forms, in fact, accounts for rather more than two per cent of industrial activity in the UK.

(Looked at in the broader context of different drugs for different societies, the argument seems less convincing. We may nod approval over attempts to wipe out cocaine production in South America, thereby stripping peasant farmers of their livelihood, while becoming hotly indignant at the prospect of a Budget increase putting the price of our bottle of gin above the weekly wage of the average Bolivian farmworker. Some societies view alcohol with just as much suspicion as we view cocaine.)

A more responsible attitude to alcohol would hardly put 750,000 people on the dole overnight. One can hardly argue, surely, that one of alcohol's great benefits to society is that it keeps this number of people in work. Besides, the more forward looking of the drinks companies themselves already realize they will have to move towards less alcoholic drinks for long-term survival. Our total liquid intake would be the same and would probably provide more or less the same employment opportunities – and possibly, to judge from the ingenuity of the pricing of most new drinks concoctions, greater profit margins.

The same could not be said of the contribution that alcoholic drinks make to the Exchequer each year in the form of excise duties: £4,226 million or 3.8 per cent of central Government revenue in 1986 (slightly less than the 4.1 per cent now provided by duties on tobacco, and considerably less than the 40 per cent of Exchequer revenues provided by the country's drinkers by the end of the last century). VAT on alcoholic drinks contributed a further £2,250 million. This is an impressive and important contribution to the running of the country and is discussed in more detail elsewhere, but it does suggest why successive governments have been so slow to adopt a policy on alcohol abuse.

Another pro-alcohol argument centres on the value to the economy of our exported drinks. These were worth £6,489 million in 1986 and brought in just under nine per cent of the value of our total exports. And when the balance of payments on alcoholic drinks is examined in detail – all that exported Scotch as against our imports (mainly wines) – the economy benefited by more than £121 million. There are signs, though, that this balance is becoming less healthy. After France, we are by far the world's most important exporter of alcoholic drinks (almost entirely spirits). But we are also – with West Germany, and a long way behind the US – one of the world's top importers of strong drink of all kinds.

There is nothing new, of course, about an important role for drug dependency in our economy, as any history book about the course of British imperialism in India and China will indicate. Nowadays, however, we have to realize that just as our merchant activities in the Far East depended at one time on opium, some of our drinks companies are doing their best to profit from the promulgation of alcohol in cultures relatively new to it.

In this context, 200 years counts as relatively new. In 1825, as sensitive a gourmet as Brillat-Savarin observed about alcohol: "It has already become a formidable weapon in our hands, for the nations of the New World have been subdued and destroyed almost as much by brandy as by firearms." Strong stuff indeed.

The brewing of strong British beers under licence in Africa may not contribute much to trade figures, but the continuing increase in such activities has clearly rung alarm bells within the World Health Organization, which held an international conference on alcohol in the Third World in 1981. Their aim is to encourage Third World countries to learn from the mistakes of cultures with a much longer history of drinking.

Economic arguments in favour of alcohol are on shaky ground in any case. The new temperance reformers have not found it difficult, by dint of a generous interpretation here and a little bit of speculation there, to reckon up alcohol's cost to society, including health costs, accidents and time lost to industry, at well over £1,600 million – and the media have not been slow to disseminate this arresting, if controversial, figure.

The case for the defence of drinking would be incomplete, of course, without some reference to alcohol's influence on the arts and artists, already hinted at at the beginning of this chapter. For centuries, some of the world's more talented writers, painters, actors, even singers have publicly acknowledged their – debt to? dependence on? – alcohol. It is difficult to separate fact from fancy here. Did the drink make them creative, or merely calm their shaking hands sufficiently to give them a firm grasp on pen or paintbrush?

Artists are probably heavier drinkers than the population in general. (Certainly "authors, journalists and related workers" were found to have an even higher rate of deaths from liver cirrhosis than "medical practitioners" in Martin Plant's study for *Risk Factors in Employment*.) But is drinking heavier among the really talented ones? Is there a genuine causal relationship between alcohol and inspiration, or just peer pressure to consume? This is one of the many fascinating questions to which scientific rigour is unlikely ever to be applied. The only people with a vested interest in proving a causal relationship are exactly those who would see no point in doing so. We may continue to wonder about the output of the likes of Francis Bacon, Malcolm Lowry, Dylan Thomas and generations of creativity before them, had they never touched a drop.

Perhaps at this point we can most relevantly look at what one of the world's more famously boozy writers, James Boswell, wrote about his muse (his most famous subject had other, less indulgent ideas) in the *London Magazine* in 1780: "Writing upon Drinking is in one respect, I think, like Drinking itself: one goes on imperceptibly, without knowing where to stop . . . ."

Drink can, indeed, be a most glorious thing, an oiler of the wheels of sociability, relaxation and life in general. The problem is that it can so swiftly turn into a demon. By its very nature, it tends to thwart good resolve. It is so deliciously easy for a moderate drinker to become a dependent drinker. The aim of this book is simply to encourage a new respect for alcohol, and to make us at long last look it in the face.

CHAPTER THREE

Alcohol and Other Drugs

Putting Alcohol In Its Place

In the autumn of 1986 the Royal College of Psychiatrists published a considerably expanded update of its 1979 *Alcohol and Alcoholism*, its first report on how those working in mental health viewed the drinking habits of the nation. Seven years on, the committee behind the report came up with the considerably more arresting title *Alcohol: Our Favourite Drug* (although, in fact, caffeine is arguably a more likely candidate for this dubious accolade).

The British drinks trade was furious about this slur on its raison d'être, nicely illustrating some of the self-delusion that makes rational comment on the world of drink and drugs so difficult. Most Europeans and members of European-based cultures such as North America, Australia and New Zealand find it difficult to accept the undoubted truth that alcohol is a drug because alcohol is *our* drug, a familiar pick-me-up woven into every strand of the fabric of society rather than a substance we are brought up to regard as wicked such as heroin, cocaine and cannabis, which have all been imported from other cultures.

The standard, and often apoplectic, response to this thesis has been that imported drugs have much worse effects when taken to excess than alcohol. Sadly, the case against drink on the grounds of the total damage wrought by alcohol abuse both medically and socially, even economically, is now being spelt out—perhaps too loudly but certainly clearly—in reports such as those from the Royal Colleges. And while the awful, if still relatively small-scale, effects of heroin and cocaine on contemporary Western society are all too obvious, no truly objective observer could find much evidence of real harm done to individuals or society by cannabis.

As Dr Michael Gossop, of the Drug Dependency Clinical Research and Treatment Unit at Maudsley Hospital, London, points out in his *Living with Drugs*, updated in 1987, the only real threat to the health of the cannabis user is the paraquat sprayed on the crops by the Mexican government in its efforts to wipe out this non-European drug. Significantly, the World Health Organization's report on its 1986 Conference of Ministers of Health on Narcotic and Psychotropic Drug Misuse devotes a page and a half to alcohol misuse, but just seven lines to cannabis.

Cannabis is probably the most widely used illicit drug in "European" societies. In the late seventies, more than half of all Americans between 18 and 25 and about a third of all British university students had tried it. A *New Society* survey found that 17 per cent of even "the Thatcher generation" had tried it. Being corralled in the same outlawed category as other much more potent and equally illegal non-European drugs has undoubtedly done it harm by association.

We have not always been so wary of cannabis. Queen Victoria's physician, Dr J. R. Reynolds, described it as "one of the most valuable medicines we possess". In 1894 the Indian Hemp Commission, set up to report on the cannabis-using habits of such a high proportion of the Queen's subjects in India, gave the substance a seven-volume all clear. "The moderate use practically produces no ill-effects ... " and there were "facts which combine to show most clearly how little injury society has hitherto sustained from hemp drugs."

These points are made not to eulogize cannabis – "turning on" seems so often to mean switching off – but simply to illustrate how irrational and transitory are conventional attitudes to drugs, and therefore laws concerning them. The Indian Hemp Commission's report, for example, was followed within months by the equally detailed but equally tolerant Royal Commission on Opium. The worthy Victorian gentlemen who had to pronounce on cannabis and opium could not have been uninfluenced by the vital part played by opium in British trade in the Far East.

Opium trading financed another British addiction: to tea. But opium was also commonly taken in Britain – not just by Byron, Coleridge, Keats, Lamb, De Quincey, Scott, Shelley and even, addictively, by Wilberforce, but much more widely for both medicinal and recreational purposes by the common people. In 1850, when the opium poppy was cultivated quite legally in much of East Anglia, Charles Kingsley wrote about the number of wives on market day in Cambridge buying their "pennord o'elevation". The *Morning Chronicle* described "the opium-eating city of Ely", where "the sale of laudanum . . . was as common as the sale of butter and cheese." No less august a body as the Royal Horticultural Society awarded prizes for particularly successful opium growing.

Within a century, our attitude towards opiates has changed considerably, especially since 1874 when heroin was literally first cooked up (in Praed Street, London). But even though societies are capable of absorbing or rejecting (or both) alien drugs, just about every society on earth has found and developed at least one indigenous psychoactive substance and many have or have had several. Only Eskimo culture seems to be devoid of any traditional mind-altering chemical substance – chiefly, presumably, because of the extreme limitations of the climate on plant life.

In the world's more hospitable climates, about 4,000 different plants can be persuaded, in some form, to alter man's mental state. (That much -thumbed work in any reference library, *The High Times Encyclopedia of Recreational Drugs*, points out that nutmeg, for example, can induce a trance-like state – although surely only in masochists, for at least 20 grams is needed.) Other than the fermentable substances that can be persuaded to transform themselves into alcohol, only about 40 products of nature have been regularly harnessed by various cultures to provide them with any sort of "high", and almost all of them are non-European in origin.

As in so many other fields (although not, hearteningly, alcoholic drinks) the traditional, naturally occurring examples have been adapted for modern use and joined by more recent synthetics. Laudanum was a useful Victorian cocktail of opium and alcohol. The khat, an evergreen shrub, of northeastern Africa, and the betel nut of India, for example, are amphetamine-like prototypes of the "speed" of the sixties. Californians who experimented with mescaline soon after were following the Aztec tradition of eating a cactus with hallucinogenic properties called peyotl.

LSD was first synthesized in 1943, considerably earlier than either the considerably more popular synthetics Librium or Valium, which are certainly psychoactive drugs and which are already as integrated into Western cultures as barbiturates such as Tuinal, Seconal, Amytal and Nembutal. LSD remains beyond the pale of social acceptability but, interestingly, our attitude to tranquillizers and barbiturates today is very similar to the common European attitude to those drugs that were "new" in the sixteenth and seventeenth centuries, tobacco and caffeine. When Jean Nicot introduced the American tobacco plant to the court of Catherine de Medici in 1561, and when tea and coffee first arrived in London in 1652, they were consumed entirely, or at least ostensibly, for medical reasons.

Tea contains only about half as much of the potentially harmful psychoactive drug caffeine as coffee, but even tea was regarded as a suspicious foreign substance at first. In 1678 Henry Savile described tea as a base, unworthy and filthy substitute for man's only suitable libation, wine. In 1756 Jonas Hanway, founder of The Marine Society, published his "Essay on Tea, considered as pernicious to HEALTH, obstructing INDUSTRY and impoverishing the NATION", a description which sounds eerily familiar today. Even as late as the early nineteenth century, tea was reviled by some physicians as a "most deadly poison".

Tobacco opened to equally mixed reviews, and since its introduction to Europe has inspired probably a greater variety of reaction than any other drug. In the seventeenth century, smokers were tortured in Russia, executed in Germany and pilloried in Turkey – clearly 200 years ahead of most Western societies in this respect.

Most imported drugs have swung in and out of favour in European societies, but alcohol has occupied a privileged position – principally because it has been around for so long. This may have been largely because of grapes' natural tendency to ferment, and the fact that the vine could be grown so easily and economically in so much of Europe, but there seems to be more to it than that. All over the world, man seems to have sought out quite early and quite deliberately some means of intoxication, some escape route from normality, like checking out a plane's emergency exits before a flight.

The first reference to the psychoactive properties of cannabis, for example, was made around 1400BC and the known history of beermaking is at least as old as that of winemaking, even though there is nothing spontaneous about it. Clay tablets demonstrate that beer was prescribed by Sumerian physicians more than 2,000 years BC, and perhaps its discovery was no less accidental than that of the kava or yangona native to South Pacific islands such as Tahiti and Fiji.

As part of a highly ritualized ceremony, the islands' most mordant young people traditionally chewed the root of a sort of pepper plant, their saliva doing a similar conversion job to the saliva of grain-chewers in very early beermaking, converting the non-fermentable starch into fermentable sugars. The chewed root was spat out into a bowl and moistened with water or coconut before this nonalcoholic but intoxicating drink was passed around, but only according to a very precise pattern. Islands such as Fiji, which persisted with their ritualized indigenous intoxicant but did not succumb, like Tahiti in the late eighteenth century, to a sudden and uncontrolled introduction of alcohol, remained much more stable.

Each society adapts itself to the indigenous drug or drugs and can easily be thrown out of kilter by the introduction of a new, imported one. Among some Aborigines and North American Indians, for instance, alcohol, a drug that is still relatively new to them, especially in distilled form, could be said to be the root of all evil.

The odd thing is that even though animals can be taught to appreciate and even depend on psychoactive drugs such as alcohol, only man seems to have the need to seek out such an escape route. Accepting this need is probably the first step towards a mature and responsible attitude to exercising it, but it is particularly difficult for Europeans, who tend to regard altered mental states as a barbarian delusion.

As Brian Inglis, author and historian, argued in *The Forbidden Game*, religion has probably played at least as important a part as botany in dictating the choice of psychoactive drug for each society. After all, societies have not necessarily confined themselves to indigenous drugs, as witness the British love affair with tea.

In South America, land of such hallucinogenic drugs as coca, peyotl and ololiuqui (morning glory), these powerful substances were traditionally in the hands of licensed handlers: priests, medicine men, shamans. Hallucinations and visions were an integral part of the South and Central American religious experience; drug-induced trances were familiar to and expected by society. Coca was an integral part of Inca religious festivals, just as the Indians living in what is now Mexico used peyotl and ololiuqui to communicate with their gods. They provided a useful direct line to the future and the past.

Then the Spaniards arrived, complete with their religion into which another drug, the transubstantiated blood of Christ, had just as effectively been woven. Anything that delivered visions apparently outside and independent of the accepted religion of Spain and Europe had to be inimical to it, and had to be suppressed. And therefore, because of the Conquistadors, alcohol overtook peyotl and eventually coca as the socially acceptable and legally condoned drug of the Americas.

Various regional ferments, and therefore alcohol, were already known in South and Central America when the Spaniards arrived but their drinking was carefully prescribed by ritual, tradition and religion, rather as the Fiji islanders treated their yangona. In these cultures, alcohol was treated with the respect it deserves, but the invading Europeans were not slow to see how useful alcohol could be to them.

The Americas were overwhelmed by wine and, later, by distilled spirits, the pre-Hispanic emperor of Mexico denouncing "the wine known as 'octli'" as: "The root and source of all evil and of all perdition ... Drunkenness is the cause of all the adulteries, rapes, corruption of virgins, and fights with relatives and friends ... all the thefts and robberies and banditry and violence; cursing and lying and gossip and slander, and of clamouring, quarrels and shouting." This pattern was to be repeated farther north several centuries later when "firewater" was used to overwhelm North American Indians, whose own drug had been tobacco.

Throughout the history of conquest, alcohol has been a powerful weapon. In their push eastwards, the Russians used vodka to blur the mushroom-induced visions of Siberian shamans. The colonization of Australia would have been considerably more difficult had alcohol not been a dangerous novelty to the Aborigines. The Amazon was conquered partly by weaning the Brazilian Indians off their gentle fermented manioc and on to the very much stronger cachaca rum.

Drugs of all kinds have played an enormous part in the world's history, and it is a very obvious symptom of the dominance of European culture that the most popular drugs of European and European-based cultures – alcohol, nicotine and caffeine – are so widely and freely accepted compared to most other drugs. Their sale may be controlled and often taxed, but they are fully embraced by the law and society.

Because of this, as the Royal College of Psychiatrists points out, there is a marked difference in society's attitudes to those who deal in different drugs. Those who work in the drinks trade, the tobacco industry and the coffee and tea business are simply salesmen in industries subject to few international controls. Meanwhile, we label as "traffickers", because they are outside the law at the moment, those who sell opiates or cannabis: drugs that have at one time been embraced in Asia and the world of Islam respectively while alcohol was seen as the wicked foreign drug.

The Psychiatrists also point out that when things go wrong with the drugs we regard as alien, we blame the drug itself. When a drunk driver kills a child, or a family is broken up by excessive drinking, we don't blame alcohol, we blame the user, saying that he (unlike us) didn't know how to handle the drug. We need not be ashamed of this apparent illogicality. Other cultures based on other drugs have done the same.

Throughout much of the Eastern world, alcohol is regarded with as much repugnance as we view opiates. To most Muslims and Hindus, our tolerance of a drug repudiated by their religions must seem extraordinary. Those thousands who live in Britain must be puzzled by our hysterical reaction to heroin, by our witch-hunting of those who use cannabis, such a contained fact of life in many parts of the Eastern world.

The beleaguered charity Action on Alcohol Abuse keeps salutory figures on British government spending on the related "problem" per death directly linked to the use of various drugs. In 1986 the public spend worked out at £35 for each tobacco-related death, £106 for each death related to alcohol, and a thought-provoking £960,000 for each death caused by solvents and those drugs that are (now) illegal in British society.

CHAPTER FOUR

C_2H_5OH

What Is Alcohol?

Kohl eye pencils, glue-sniffing, cholesterol and antifreeze are some of the unlikely ingredients in the unexpurgated story of alcohol, or at least of that large family known chemically speaking as alcohols. To chemists, alcohols are organic compounds which contain a hydroxyl group attached to a saturated carbon atom. They comprise a wide but usually distinctly unappetizing variety of permutations of hydrogen, carbon and oxygen.

One of the most commercially important alcohols, for instance, is methanol, also known as methyl alcohol or wood alcohol and the active ingredient in methylated spirits or "meths". It is a useful solvent and antifreeze but also extremely toxic – as was fatally demonstrated in Italy's wine scandal of 1986. Other common alcohols include glycerol, lactic acid, sorbitol and certain higher alcohols which are among the active ingredients appreciated by solvent abusers. Many alcohols are commonly found in nature as esters, or combinations of alcohols and acids such as that newish bogeyman cholesterol, a solid alcohol closely related to the bile acids. Vitamin A_1 also qualifies as an alcohol.

To non-chemists, however, alcohol means ethyl alcohol or ethanol, the only potable member of the alcohol family. Although we know it best as a stimulating drink, it also has wide industrial applications in the perfume and cosmetic businesses, in solvents and even as a substitute for petrol.

("Gasahol" has been mooted as a – rather uneconomic – way of draining the European wine lake.)

Although some members of the temperance movement in the last century did their best to prove that the word alcohol was derived from the Arabic *al gul* for a desert demon, evil spirit or ghoul, it is generally accepted that it comes from another Arabic expression, *al kuhl*, for the dark eye powder we now know as kohl. Originally *kuhl* meant any very fine powder, but by the sixteenth century it had come to mean the essence of something, just as the fine residue of a solid was then thought to be its essential substance. Arab alchemists introduced the art of distillation and when it was applied to liquids, and in particular wine, *alcool vini* denoted the very essence of wine. By the end of the eighteenth century, when the art of distillation came to be widely understood, alcohol was the term given to any liquid that had been distilled and therefore converted to its essence. Chemists in the mid-nineteenth century then called the entire family of alcohols after its most famous member, distinguishing that particular alcohol with the prefix ethyl because it can be converted into ether.

In common English usage now, alcohol effectively means ethyl alcohol – although the French use the word *alcools* specifically to denote distilled spirits (thus neatly taking wine, a major factor in the French economy, out of the line of direct fire in any anti-alcohol campaign).

The chemical formula for ethyl alcohol is C_2H_5OH, and a neat chemical equation can be used as a satisfactory shorthand for the series of extremely complex biochemical reactions which produce it.

$$C_6H_{12}O_6 \rightarrow 2C_2H_5OH + 2CO_2$$
glucose   alcohol   carbon dioxide

This shows in broad terms how sugar can be transformed into alcohol and gas by the process of fermentation. As outlined in Chapter Nine, man was drinking the products of fermentation long before he had any idea how it worked. Any mulch of grapes contains sugars and would start to ferment if left long enough in a warm place, the glucose being transformed into alcohol while the carbon dioxide gas bubbled off. Very basic wine thus virtually made itself in prehistoric times. Beer, the product of a similar transformation of malted barley, and other products of fermented starch were probably "discovered" equally hazardously. Alcohol occupies a special place in society in that, of all psychoactive drugs, it is the one that prehistoric man probably encountered first.

It was not until the mid-nineteenth century that scientists, most notably Pasteur, worked out what caused the transformation we know as fermentation. This could not, in any case, have been done, or at least proved, before the development of the microscope in the seventeenth century. Even 200 years later it required a giant leap of ingenuity and imagination to fly in the face of accepted chemical wisdom and posit that tiny living organisms, the self-propagating cells we now call yeasts, might be responsible.

So derisory of this new theory were the top chemists of the day that they published this anonymous spoof on the new theory, current but not established before Pasteur, in the contemporary German equivalent of *Scientific American* in 1839: "These animals have the form of a Beindorf still (without the cooling apparatus) ... From the moment that they escape from the egg, one sees that these animals swallow sugar from the surrounding solution; one can see it arrive in the stomach quite clearly. It is instantly digested, and this digestion is instantly and most definitely recognized by the subsequent expulsion of excrement. In a word, these infusoria eat sugar, empty wine alcohol from the intestinal canal, and carbonic acid [carbon dioxide] from the bladder. In the full condition, the bladder possesses the form of a champagne bottle ... "

Just over 150 years later, the initial, explanatory programme in the world's first television series on wine, *The Wine Programme*, was, quite independently, to use a model almost identical to that so sceptically outlined above to explain the process of fermentation.

Among Louis Pasteur's many seminal discoveries in varied branches of science, he was able to establish in 1857, after a rigorous programme of microscopic observation, that certain recognizable yeasts were responsible for certain fermentations, and that different sorts of cells had predictable effects on different transformations. Thus, out of the demon drink, was born the science of microbiology, vaccination and a major sector of modern medicine, the result of a diligent young man from Jura whose science-degree diploma was marked "mediocre" in chemistry.

Thousands of different strains of yeast have been identified but most of the yeasts responsible for alcoholic drinks, and indeed for most yeast-based breads, belong to the *Saccharomyces cerevisiae*, the beer type of sugar fungus: those microbes that are capable of effectively transforming sugar into alcohol with a minimum of off-odours. These, the squeaky-clean cousins of the noxious, malevolent microorganisms we call germs, seem to have been specifically designed to provide man with the tempting balm we call alcohol.

Although of all alcoholic drinks today wine seems most encumbered by the complicated trappings of scholarship and social innuendo, it has always been the simplest to produce. A cocktail of yeasts is naturally present in the atmosphere in any established wine-producing region, most notably and usefully the oval-shaped or *Ellipsoideus* strains of *Saccharomyces cerevisiae*. They are naturally to be found in the dusty "bloom" on the skin of a wine grape, so that once a grape is crushed, the sugar inside comes into contact with the yeast and, provided the temperature is high enough to persuade the yeasts to work, the process of fermentation will begin.

(All sorts of other, less benign bacteria also tend to get in on the act and, in the days before it was known how to control them by depriving them of the oxygen they need to work in, must have resulted in some fairly unappetizing flavours and characteristics in early wines. Nowadays the winemaking process can be controlled so tightly that in the newer wine regions, where a much smaller indigenous population of wine yeasts is naturally available, European yeasts are imported, specially cultured and deliberately introduced to the fermentation vat by the winemaker. The exact relationship between yeasts and flavour is still poorly understood.)

Unless it gets too hot or too cold for them, the yeasts continue to work, transforming the sugar into ethyl alcohol and the essential "waste product" carbon dioxide (which is why a slight fizz and whiff of CO_2 are usually the first signs that a pot of home-made jam in a warm cupboard is starting to ferment). Fermentation stops when all the sugar has been transformed into alcohol or when the winemaker decrees it should by suddenly cooling the nascent wine, the "must", and filtering the yeasts out of it or, in the case of very ripe grapes, when the must is so alcoholic that the yeasts no longer have the strength to continue their enzymatic work. Some yeasts are stronger than others, but most are overpowered once the alcohol level reaches 14 or 15 per cent.

It follows that the more sugar there is in the grapes, the higher the potential alcohol of the resultant wine. This is why, in very general terms, wines produced in cool, ungenerous climates contain less alcohol than those made from vines ripened closer to the equator.

Things are not quite as simple as that, however. At least, not since another French chemist, Chaptal, half a century before Pasteur's discoveries, promulgated a method of beefing up French wines at the same time as giving a huge fillip to beet-sugar production. "Chaptalization" involves adding sugar to unfermented grape must to give the yeasts even more to work on and boost the resultant wine's level of alcohol (not sugar). It is still commonly used in all French wine regions other than the deep south (which effectively means most of France's top wines), in most German wines, in New Zealand and the cooler vineyard regions of North America, often raising the final alcohol content of a wine considerably. In England, for example, wine producers have regularly been allowed to increase their wines by four and a half degrees of alcohol, say from 6.5 to 11 per cent.

The original purpose was to make wines more stable and fitter for travel. Today's winemakers in the cooler regions argue that a chaptalized wine makes a better vehicle for wine aromas, and that a wine's flavour is somehow less apparent in a weaker unchaptalized wine. Chaptalization is widely used in Bordeaux and Burgundy to compensate for the weather in cooler years when the grapes do not reach maximum ripeness. It does seem odd, however, that in a world which is trying to moderate its alcohol consumption, perhaps 20 per cent of all the wine produced in some years has its alcoholic strength deliberately and considerably increased. Did Jean André Chaptal, later Minister of the Interior and Comte de Chanteloupe under Napoleon, realize how great and long his influence would be on the livers of the world's wine drinkers?

Of course, as thousands of home winemakers know, grapes are not the only fruit that can be persuaded to make wine. But while most fruit and vegetables contain fermentable sugars, the juiciness of grapes lends itself particularly well to spontaneous winemaking. The vine can, and most effectively does, grow in poor, well-drained soil. This encourages a much deeper root system than that of most other crops, thereby giving grapes (and the resultant wine) direct access to a much more interesting palette of flavours. The fact that the vine is also capable of manifesting itself in so many different varieties, even within the single species *Vitis vinifera* which is responsible for most of the wines we drink today, makes fermented grape juice a potentially much more complex substance than the fermented juice of most other plants.

The alcohol level of grape-based unfortified or table wine varies from around seven per cent in some of Germany's unchaptalized bottlings to about 15 per cent in wines made from very ripe grapes, such as those grown around the Mediterranean. (Any nearer the equator than this and the vine will not lie dormant in winter, with disastrous effects on wine quality; much farther away than Germany and the grapes won't ripen at all, as some English vine growers know to their cost.) Wines such as sherry, port, madeira and some muscats, which have been fortified by the addition of alcohol, vary in strength from 15 or 16 per cent for the most delicate of sherries to 20 per cent alcohol for the least delicate of ports.

Wines made from other fruits vary enormously in strength, depending on the ripeness of the raw material and the amount of sugar added by the home winemaker as domestic chaptalization, but they are not usually as strong as grape-based wines. Nor do they, or home-brewed beers, figure in official statistics on alcohol consumption.

Cider – fermented apple juice – and its pear-based counterpart, perry, have been important forms of alcohol in England and Normandy and are produced by techniques that parallel those used to make wine. Cider's alcoholic content can vary from an innocuous three per cent to a potency to rival some grape-based wines.

Although more and more fuss is made about wine (a reflection, in part, of social mobility, but also of the additional complexity of the liquid itself), less and less of it is being produced worldwide. The two major producing countries, France and Italy, are responding to an acute wine surplus in much of the world by gradually pulling up their least successful but most productive vineyards. (This is to some extent being counterbalanced, however, by a dramatic increase in wine production in the USSR, now the world's third biggest producer, and a perceptible increase in vineyard area in such "new" wine-producing countries as China and Canada.)

Making beer or any other fermented cereal from scratch is a rather more complicated process (although much of the hard work is prepackaged in the kits available to today's home brewers). Beer is not simply fermented grain and water, in the way that wine is essentially fermented grape juice. The grain that is beer's raw material, usually barley, contains, in its raw state, unfermentable starch rather than fermentable sugar. And whereas grapes have quite a lot of inherent flavour, most cereals don't.

Around the world, three different ways of converting the unfermentable starches in cereals into fermentable sugars have been used. The most primitive, practised in South America and the South Pacific, is to set salivary enzymes to work on it – i.e. chew it – before fermenting it. The second, still current in the Far East, involves growing a particularly effective mould on, usually, rice.

The most common method by far, however, is that used, with many variations, by today's brewers. The grain is allowed to germinate slightly, which produces enzymes that break down the starch into sugars for the seedlings. Germination is then stopped by drying out the grain and this substance, called malt, is roasted to give it colour and flavour. Unlike all but the best-equipped vintners, the brewer can store this, his raw material, until he is ready to ferment it. At this point he soaks it in warm water to transform the starch into fermentable glucose and maltose, and calls the sweet, nonalcoholic mixture wort.

It is at this point for beer (rather than ale) that another ingredient, a distant cousin of another psychoactive drug, cannabis, is added to the wort. During the Middle Ages it was found that the resins leeched from hops helped to flavour and preserve the resultant beer, killing harmful microbes. Health-conscious drinkers owe a debt to hops for the fact that they were able to take over some of the preserving work from alcohol, and thus made lower-alcohol beers feasible.

The brewer now has his equivalent of ripe grapes ready for fermentation and introduces specially developed yeasts. Most of today's lighter beers and lagers are produced using the *Saccharomyces carlsbergensis* yeast, developed but generously not patented by the Danish brewers Carlsberg, whose technicians applied Pasteur's principles and the newly developed skills of microbiology to beer production at the end of the last century. The yeasts used for traditional English ales belong to the same family as those used by winemakers, *Saccharomyces cerevisiae* (the second word is easy to remember for those who know how to order a beer in Spanish, *cerevisia* being Latin for beer and derived from the roots of the words cereal and vigour).

Beers vary in strength from about three per cent for mild, just under four for bitter and the most popular lagers, four for stouts such as Guinness, 5.6 for "Pils" lagers and eight per cent, or as much as a light German table wine, for barley wine and strong ales such as Carlsberg Special.

The world's beer-producing capacity is limited only by its ability to grow grain and the breweries of the world have been increasing their output enormously and steadily – even though, by the mid-eighties, per capita consumption in the important beer markets Germany, Czechoslovakia and Denmark was gently dropping.

Despite the sterling work put in on behalf of the brewers by the more elliptical thinkers in London's advertising agencies, beer production in Britain has been declining markedly in favour of wine and other, more flashily marketed, new drinks. In the seventeenth century, however, beer was by far the most popular form of alcohol in Britain. By the end of that century we were drinking five times as much beer per head as we are now, although at this stage its alcoholic strength was not recorded. The dissolution of the monasteries meant that all wine had to be imported and became even more expensive, and the art of distillation was not yet widely applied to bring distilled liquors to the masses.

Wines and beers look like very puny forms of alcohol when compared with the average distilled spirit, however. Nature went no further towards providing us with alcoholic stimulation than giving us yeasts, which themselves have a self-containment mechanism in that most are overpowered in a liquid once it reaches 14 or 15 per cent alcohol (although the Kingston-upon-Thames makers of "British wine" have developed some that can work at strengths of up to 22 per cent). Man therefore had to wait until the complex business of distillation had been developed before he had the chance to see just how powerful alcohol could be. Some, certainly the early temperance workers, might argue that our livers would have been much obliged had distillation never been applied to fermented liquids (although those living in the Cognac or Armagnac districts or on Scotland's Speyside could hardly be expected to agree).

Distillation, as any schoolboy chemist knows, relies on separating substances with different boiling points by heating them to a critical temperature and condensing the vapour given off. Since alcohol has a lower boiling point than water, a heated fermented liquid gives off an even more alcoholic vapour which can be condensed into a more potent liquid.

Although there is some evidence to suggest that such a technique was applied to ancient "beers" based on rice, millet and molasses in India and the Far East as early as 800BC, the art of distillation was hardly known in the West until 15 centuries later when distillation played an important part in the Arab alchemy of the Muslims. Distillation then was applied to all sorts of substances, and was powerfully bound up with the philosophy that the essence of something, its elixir, was physically in it and could be isolated by sophisticated chemical means. Hence *al kuhl*, originally, for any fine powder or essence.

Nothing less than the elixir of life was the ultimate goal, and by about 1300 the term aqua vitae, or "water of life", had been coined for distilled wine. The French continue to call their colourless spirits eaux-de-vie, for instance, and the word whisky comes from the same expression in Gaelic *uisgebaugh*. But it took a century or more before distilled liquor could be regarded as a pleasant drink rather than a medicine.

The key here lies not only in the development of a spirit-drinking culture (which developed long after the wine- and beer-drinking cultures) but also in a technique of double distillation which produces a much smoother, more attractive – and, only incidentally, more alcoholic – spirit. The Charentais, who are responsible for cognac, the Gascons, whose native spirit is armagnac, and the Celts on behalf of their whiskies continue to dispute who first discovered this means of transporting distilled liquors from the medicine cabinet to the cocktail cabinet.

Certainly distilling expertise was an essentially Celtic craft – Scottish, Irish and Welsh origins have all been claimed and for centuries the Celts kept to themselves their whiskies, the distilled products of the mashed local grains which fermented so easily in the damp climate. It was not until well into the nineteenth century, long after the union of Scotland and England in 1707, that the two countries introduced each other to their drinking habits.

If the Scots are defined by their whisky, one of England's great gifts to the world is gin. Both spirits start off as fermented grain and come out of the still as colourless liquids, but different sorts of stills are used and, whereas whisky is aged for several years in oak casks to give it colour and flavour, gin is a comparatively youthful distillate to which flavours, notably juniper, are added. Although two of its important production centres today are in Warrington and Harlow, British gin is called London Dry to distinguish it from the heavier, more schnapps-like Dutch gin so popular in the Netherlands.

Vodka is even closer to pure alcohol. It is very like gin without the flavouring, but can be made from virtually any fermentable raw material: grain, molasses, even potatoes. Modern, Western vodka is even specially treated to remove any flavour other than that of ethyl alcohol, and it is difficult to argue that the vodka drinker is engaging in any form of connoisseurship. The flavoured vodkas of the USSR and Poland, where vodka was born, are needed for that.

Today almost every country or region (with the exception of central and southern Africa, where distilling is relatively new) has evolved its own spirit, depending on the cheapest and most plentiful suitable raw material. Normandy ferments apple juice into cider and distils that into calvados, just as applejack is distilled (sometimes even frozen) from New England apples. Throughout the Middle East, except where alcohol is forbidden by strict application of Muslim principles, palm sap, dates, grape juice, molasses and cereals are all used to provide fermented raw material from which to distil arrack, arak, raki and ouzo, usually flavoured with aniseed – and found in more refined form in France as pastis, Pernod and now even in dealcoholized form. In Scandinavia and northern Germany, the indigenous spirit is akvavit or schnapps, a grain distillate, often flavoured and often strong. Mexico has its tequila, based on the fermented juice of the cactus-like agave, which is itself drunk there, at beer-like strength, as pulque. And in the torrid sugar-cane producing zone rum is, of course, the staple spirit, made from fermented sugar-cane juice or molasses.

But perhaps the most widely produced spirit is based on fermented grape juice or wine – of which the world now has a serious and ready surplus. Brandy is the generic term, but no spirit varies as much in quality. Cognac and armagnac, produced similarly but with differences that are considered worth duelling over by some aficionados, constitute brandy in its finest form. Indeed, these are the spirits for connoisseurship, together with pure malt whisky (as opposed to the usual blended Scotch which is lightened with a lesser spirit called grain whisky).

A good example of brandy at its considerably less inspiring is the European alcohol lake, into which the European wine lake of surplus inferior wine has been distilled – chiefly because spirits take up less storage space than wine. This basic raw grape spirit, unsoftened by years of gentle maturation in small oak casks, is so embarrassingly plentiful that it is quite cheap. In fact, all but the most carefully matured distilled spirits are extremely cheap to produce; it is only the world's tax systems which, perhaps quite rightly, make them seem so expensive. The availability of inexpensive hooch has, in recent years, inspired a burgeoning family of new alcoholic concoctions such as Bailey's Irish Cream and Malibu in which alcohol is just one of many added ingredients, along with extremely sophisticated marketing.

The gulf between the fantasy woven by the advertising agencies and the reality that comes clinking off the bottling line has done nothing to help the drinker who wants to monitor his intake of alcohol. Nor has the fact that the Americans, the British and most Europeans have used three different systems to denote alcoholic strength. The British "proof" system, almost incredibly, evolved from the strength at which a mixture of the spirit and gunpowder would explode. It has taken us until May 1988 to catch up with the European law that all alcoholic drinks must be labelled with their alcoholic strength in percentage of alcohol by volume.

The normal strength for gins, rums, brandies and whiskies is 40 per cent, 70° proof or 80° US proof, although (Westernized) vodka has customarily been sold at less than that. There is nothing magical about this strength; most spirits come off the still considerably stronger. This just happens to be the commonly agreed strength to which they are "broken", i.e. watered, down. Even more than with wine, there is potential here, in a world which seems increasingly concerned with alcohol consumption, for making an extremely simple reduction at a stroke. Lloyd George effected just this during World War I when the strength of most British spirits was reduced from 43 to 40 per cent .

Most gins, whiskies, rums and brandies which are bottled at less than normal strength at the moment are unfortunately simply very mediocre spirits, designed for the keenest shopper. Some spirits for the cognoscenti, such as particularly recherché malt whiskies, are bottled even stronger than the norm, however – and Majorca's gift to the spirituous world, cana, is a lethally flammable 75 per cent.

There seems little limit to the world's potential production of spirits, although it is far more tightly controlled than the production of wine and beer – in theory, at least. This is not just because governments have more excise duty to lose from illicit distillation, but because distillation is a potentially dangerous business which, unlike fermentation, can easily produce toxic substances – as each year's crop of moonshine fatalities testifies.

The global picture of spirits production is remarkably similar to that of brewing, with half being produced in Europe, more than 20 per cent in North America, and Africa and Oceania being unimportant. During the 1970s stills in just three countries, the UK, the USA and the USSR, turned out almost 40 per cent of the world's spirits.

No drinker should be unaware that alcoholic drink production is big business. Two business writers, John Cavanagh and Frederick F. Clairmonte, devoted a book, *Alcoholic Beverages – Dimensions of Corporate Power*, to showing just how concentrated is the balance of power in the world of drink. In 1985 they put the global worth of the drinks business at $170 billion, with a relatively modest global advertising expenditure of $2 billion.

The symbiotic elements of production and consumption in the drinks industry generate several huge areas of scientific study. No one who has sat through a seminar on yeast technology, or a symposium on the effect of oak provenance in cognac maturation, could deny that these are extremely sober, not to say dull, affairs.

CHAPTER FIVE

What Alcohol Does to Individuals

Lifting the Lid, or What Drink Really Does to Our Minds

One of the main reasons why alcoholic drinks are so popular, why alcohol is the world's most widely embraced mind-changing substance, is that it seems to stimulate us. It stimulates social intercourse of all sorts. It makes us feel better able to cope with specific problems and with social life in general. It broadens the horizons of possibility and gives us the impression we can achieve more than we can without it.

Yet in medical terms alcohol, unlike amphetamine ("speed") or caffeine (coffee), it is far from a stimulant. In many ways it falls into the same category as narcotics, barbiturates and anaesthetics. Strictly speaking, it is a depressant which actually reduces the activity of the central nervous system and in particular the workings of the brain.

In fact, alcohol sedates, as any lunchtime drinker finds out in mid-afternoon, and tranquillizes, as anyone who has ever treated an external injury with an internal tot of brandy knows. But alcohol initially makes us feel more excited and animated because its most immediately obvious depressant effect is to suppress the mechanisms that usually control, or keep a lid on, our inhibitions. The feeling that drinking "takes the lid off" our normal behaviour is therefore particularly appropriate, however discomforting it may seem to many of us that we have other, more sociable, inebriated personalities that are kept tightly in check throughout our sober lives. It also helps to explain why we all react in such different ways under the influence: some raucous, some maudlin, some loquacious, some sullen. Our drunken behaviour very much depends on what happens to be lurking under the lid.

It also depends, interestingly, on how we feel we ought to behave when inebriated. In our culture we most commonly associate behaviour that is animated, talkative and generally socially flirtatious (with or without the sexual connotation) with drink. In cultures in other parts of the world, Aboriginal and North American Indian groups, for example, alcohol is more commonly associated with torpor and its soporific effects, and that is how members of those cultures react. Low-alcohol ferments may, by tradition, be designed for communal ritual in such cultures, but higher-alcohol drinks are for solitary oblivion.

Even within Britain, there are discernible subcultures within which people are taught to associate aggression and violence with drink. Hence football hooliganism and Saturday night pub warfare, as a counterpart to the apparently stimulating intellectual discussion or amusing gossip around dinner tables in other British subcultures. (Even more amazing, as evidence of the weird and wonderful ways in which alcohol affects us, is the fact that we take on our inebriated personality even if given placebos rather than alcoholic drink.)

Alcohol is unusually good at diffusing widely and evenly into our bodily tissues (which is why Breathalyzers are considered to be so accurate: the concentration of alcohol in the lungs is in direct proportion to the concentration of alcohol in the bloodstream). Alcohol is potent enough to alter the structure of our cell walls, making them more fluid. This interferes with the way things as important as nerve signals and chemicals used in the metabolic process are transmitted through our cells, which most obviously manifests itself as lack of coordination and the other behavioural clues that (sober) people observe in the inebriated.

The action of alcohol on our cell walls to slow the transmission of nerve signals is one of the most powerful explanations of why our reactions slow and our speech tends to slur under the influence of drink. The euphoric disinhibiting effect of alcohol convinces us we are *more* capable under the influence of a drink or two, but the depression of the nervous system actually makes us less so, as many experiments have demonstrated.

It has been shown that drivers with less than the legal limit of alcohol in their systems need to add up to 30 feet of "thinking distance" to the distance needed to stop, in order to allow for their more lethargic reactions to road hazards. In one oft-quoted simulated driving exercise, bus drivers quite happily proposed driving their buses through gaps far too narrow when the alcohol concentration in their blood was only 50mg/100ml – a level that could be reached after three "units" of alcohol (a unit being very roughly half a pint of beer, a small glass of wine or a single pub measure of spirits). In those who are most susceptible to the effects of alcohol, the risk of a traffic accident starts to accelerate rapidly at only 30mg/100ml, or after two drinks. This is the level at which almost everyone's reaction times start to slow.

At the maximum permitted blood-alcohol level for drivers, 80mg/100ml, reached after drinking five units in an hour, almost everyone is medically intoxicated, and many people's driving ability is materially impaired. Which is why there is a very good case for making domestic breathalysers much more widely available, and accurate – and possibly, some think, for lowering the maximum legal blood-alcohol level.

Someone with a concentration of 100mg/100ml is usually observably inebriated, and at a level as high as 200mg/100ml would be very obviously clumsy and emotionally impaired. At 300mg/100ml, most people would be grossly intoxicated and would then pass out. Those who didn't, and somehow managed to continue to drink, would die or go into a coma at a blood-alcohol concentration of about 500mg/ml.

These blood-alcohol concentrations can, very roughly, be translated into specific intake, but they all depend on the ability of the drinker to cope with alcohol and on when and how it is drunk. One unit of alcohol (eight grams) results in a peak blood-alcohol concentration of *about* 15mg/100ml in most men and 20mg/100ml in most women. Alcohol is removed from the blood at the rate of about 15mg/100ml an hour. So for men it would take seven or eight units drunk in an hour to get up to a blood-alcohol level of 100mg/100ml, and between 15 and 20 units – two bottles of wine, say – drunk in an hour to get the body's blood-alcohol level up to the general pass-out rate of 300mg/ml.

In general, therefore, it takes about an hour to rid the blood of the alcohol in one drink. So any man wanting to remain below the legal driving limit should not take more than five units of alcohol and a woman not more than four, unless they are spaced at the rate of only one unit per hour. After a binge of, say, 12 units (six pints, six doubles or a bottle and a third of wine), the drinker is still under the influence of alcohol 12 hours later, which in practice can mean that some people are not entirely sober even when they drive to work. Similarly, a woman who drank a whole bottle of wine at a dinner party may well find that she is over the legal driving limit until a full five hours after their last drink. A sobering thought.

The trouble is, however, that we all vary so much in our ability to cope with alcohol. This, of course, is widely but probably often erroneously used by individuals to excuse their overindulgence: the "Oh, I'm lucky, I can take it" syndrome. It seems sensible for anyone who drinks to learn as much as possible about how and when they are most sensitive to its effects, although research in this important area is by no means complete.

There are many other factors, not least of which, of course, is how the alcohol was drunk, over what time period, what sort of alcohol it was and whether it was taken on an empty stomach. Most experiments on blood-alcohol concentrations are conducted in very atypical circumstances. To investigate the body's ability to deal with alcohol, the required dose is administered, often all at once, and the resulting blood-alcohol concentrations logged over the succeeding hours. In fact, most of us take in our alcohol much more slowly, often mitigating its ill-effects by eating and/or drinking nonalcoholic drinks. But there is also the frequent practice of serial drinking, most obviously at lunch and then dinner, resulting in what might be called the "top-up effect" of alcohol in the bloodstream. Someone who drinks, say, four units at lunchtime will still have sufficient alcohol in the blood to make a further four units taken in the evening push the blood-alcohol level over the legal driving limit.

There is an urgent need for research that more closely simulates actual social behaviour.

As can already be deduced, however, to minimize the ill-effects of alcohol, and to maintain its pleasantly euphoric effect, the key is to sip alcoholic drinks as slowly as possible. If a drinker really goes at it and, say, by downing five pints or a bottle of fairly potent wine in an hour, manages to get his blood-alcohol level up to about 150mg/100ml, he may well appear to be behaving normally but will be unable to recall what he did or, in medical terminology, will experience an amnesic episode.

I remember, or rather I do not remember, the second half of a summer's evening at Oxford, thanks to one college's deceptively innocuous-tasting mix of orange juice, gin and Cointreau (demonstrating all too painfully how dangerous these cocktails of incalculable strength are). Most of us are only too uncomfortably aware that we have less than perfect recall of what is said around a well-lubricated dinner table. Many general population surveys have shown that more than 15 per cent of interviewees confess to an alcohol-induced blackout in the previous year. Repeated and regular blacking out may well be a sign that a social drinker is becoming a problem drinker.

The mortifying mechanisms of memory loss are not properly understood, and nor are the mechanisms that explain the following near-converse of that process. Psychologists, who always seem to be messing about with apparently bizarre experiments, have found that if we are taught things when we are intoxicated, we are much more likely to remember them when we are reintoxicated than when we are sober. This process, which they call state-dependent learning, may well explain why some people seem able to drive even when heavily intoxicated. They may acquire the knack of drunken driving as a special state-dependent learning process, dreadful thought though this is. Such compartmentalized living would certainly help to explain the Jekyll-and-Hyde syndrome: why some people's skills, predilections and even characters when drunk seem so different from when they are sober.

Other experiments have shown that alcohol, even in quite low doses, can quite severely affect our vision. Long before the "seeing double" phase, our focusing ability and our ability to follow the path of moving objects is seriously affected, which does nothing to ease the problem of drunken driving. At higher blood-alcohol levels, our ability to distinguish between different shades and intensities of light is impaired, with our sensitivity to red – the stop-light colour, unfortunately – being particularly badly affected. We also lose sensitivity to complex flavours and smells, and even to nuances of sound. Such things are known because they are easy to measure.

A Tantalizing Discovery

Until very recently, the theory that alcohol's apparent stimulation derived from its suppression of the brain's controls on our inhibitions was just that, an attractively convincing theory. In 1985, however, scientists at Hoffmann-La Roche discovered a drug that not only provided solid evidence for this theory, but was also tantalizingly close to a substance that man has been seeking for almost as long as he has been drinking: something that will reverse the effects of alcohol.

Most of the third book of Aristotle's *Problemata* was concerned with the mysteries of drinking and drunkenness, and even posited that cabbage water could ward off drunkenness. The Ancient Greeks believed that a particular purple precious stone would ward off drunkenness: their word for it, amethyst, means literally "not drunken". Modern scientists have been experimenting in recent years with various substances they call "amethystic agents" (about which more elsewhere), but the most promising so far is Hoffmann-La Roche's RO15-4513.

It is significant that the tale of RO15-4513 was reported in the *New Scientist* under the heading: "The spirit is lucid but the flesh is drunk". This derivative of benzodiazepine is received by the part of the brain that receives the brain's principal inhibitory neurotransmitter, γ(gamma)-aminobutyric acid (GABA), the chief control on our inhibitions. GABA controls the movement of chloride ions in the brain cells. After detailed work on RO15-4513, the researchers believe that what alcohol does is to stimulate, by its effect on the cell walls, the GABA receptor to allow more chloride ions into the brain cells, thereby loosening inhibitions. But if RO15-4513 is introduced, it binds to the GABA receptor and blocks any effect of alcohol on it. So there is no loosening of inhibitions, and no feeling of being inebriated. The substance shows every sign of returning the intoxicated to complete composure only minutes after being taken.

This could be good news – nay, wonderful news – for anyone who wanted to drive home "sober" from a dinner party, or get a good afternoon's work done after a bibulous lunch. But there is, needless to say, a snag.

RO15-4513 may be a superb GABA antagonist, but it does nothing to stave off alcohol's ravages on the body, which is why it still has its cumbersome laboratory name rather than being a sellout at our local chemist as "Soberup" or "Debinge". Quite apart from the obvious ethical difficulty of marketing something that might encourage us along the road to cirrhosis, there is the problem that RO15-4513 has the side-effect of increasing the likelihood of convulsions – to which severe alcohol abusers (such as we might all be tempted to become were RO15-4513 commercially available) are already more prone than average.

How Alcohol Works In the Body

When we swallow an alcoholic drink it shoots down the digestive tract and into the stomach, from which alcohol is absorbed into all the body tissues, and into the small intestine, from which it is absorbed even more rapidly than from the stomach. Unlike most foods, it is not digested but, because of its ability to move freely around the body, passes straight into the bloodstream without undergoing any change at all.

The effects of alcohol are greatest or, to put it another way, one feels most drunk, when the concentration of alcohol in the blood – and a wide range of body tissues such as heart, brain and muscles – is highest. Less than five per cent of the alcohol we ingest leaves the body as untreated alcohol, either in urine or slightly boozy breath. All the rest has to be burnt up, or metabolized.

It is in the liver that the burning-up process of removing alcohol from the body takes place, which is why liver damage is often one of the first signs of physiological damage wrought by alcohol. The portal system of blood vessels designed to drain the stomach and intestines carries the alcohol to the liver, together with any other digested food which may be in the system. In the liver cells the alcohol is broken down and oxidized (or burnt up) under the action of an interesting enzyme called alcohol dehydrogenase, or ADH, which our bodies have been given with apparently that sole purpose.

It is tempting to see the presence of ADH as evidence that man has been drinking alcohol for so long that the process of evolution has had to provide him with a means of coping with it. However, man's history of drinking may be too short to have that sort of evolutionary impact, and it seems much more likely that we have ADH in our bodies to cope with the small amounts of alcohol that are naturally formed by the complexities of our inner workings. ADH is needed to break down these inner alcohols – its presence in the liver purifies the blood of even a teetotaller – which is presumably why we have not been supplied with very much ADH, and certainly not enough to cope efficiently and rapidly with the amounts of alcohol commonly drunk of an evening.

Even working at full tilt, ADH can only break down and remove alcohol from the blood at the rate of about eight grams of alcohol, or 15mg/100ml, or one "unit" of alcohol (less for women) an hour. So to maintain the most attractive effects of alcohol, the initial gently euphoric high, it would be sensible to drink no more than one unit of alcohol, a modest glass of wine, say, in every hour. And to ensure that one stays below the legal limit for driving, 80mg/100ml, it is advisable to drink less than five units of alcohol (probably only three or four units for women) and to wait for at least an hour after finishing the last alcoholic drink. But this is necessarily vague. Each of us has a different metabolic rate, and this can vary in different situations and even for women at different stages of the menstrual cycle. Our reactions are impaired even after one unit of alcohol. The safest course is not to combine drinking with driving at all.

Each individual varies enormously in the amount of ADH they have, for instance – the bigger and healthier the liver, the better – and in the efficiency with which it works. There is strong, although not particularly scientific, evidence to suggest that genetics play a part, and that some people are simply born with a more efficient alcohol metabolism than others. Heavy drinkers who have not suffered liver damage seem to get their bodies into condition as though metabolizing alcohol were a sport and tend to remove it faster than average from the blood – although after the onset of liver damage, the metabolic rate rapidly declines. This explains why heavy drinkers appear to go into a sudden and marked decline as a result of the ravages of alcohol. The average liver will still leave some alcohol in the blood eight hours after six units of alcohol have been consumed. Even more determined drinkers can well find themselves over the limit when driving to work the morning after a particularly heavy session. And those who drink, say, 16 units a day will never clear their blood of alcohol. It is largely to give the liver a chance to "dry out" that doctors recommend two or three days' abstinence each week. In fact, within reasonable limits it is generally thought to be better for the liver to veer more towards binge drinking than little-and-often sipping.

A given amount of alcohol's impact on the body is governed by several factors other than the efficiency of the drinker's alcohol metabolism, and in particular the liver, including the form in which the alcohol was taken; the other contents of the stomach; other drugs which may have been ingested; the state of the drinker's gastric system; the drinker's sex, weight and proportion of fat.

Why It's Tough Being a Woman

Long before the emotive question of alcohol and pregnancy becomes an issue, women find themselves at a serious disadavantage when it comes to drinking. This is partly, but only partly, because women tend to be smaller and lighter than men. On average, women weigh 15 per cent less than men. It follows that the smaller a body, the less the body fluid, the more concentrated a given amount of alcohol will be, and the more intoxicated one feels and the more harm the toxicity of alcohol will inflict.

There is also the nasty fact that women's bodies tend to have a higher proportion of subcutaneous fat, about 25 per cent as opposed to an average of 15 per cent in men. This difference is probably to provide us with the ability to adapt ourselves to the differing nutritional demands of pregnancy and feeding babies. Alcohol hardly enters fat because of its low blood supply, so a given amount of alcohol will be concentrated in a smaller amount of body fluid in a woman than in a man of exactly the same weight. Quite apart from actual weight variation, women tend to have only about 50 per cent of their weight made up of body fluid, whereas the proportion in young men (often society's most enthusiastic drinkers) is 60 per cent. So alcohol is much more concentrated in a woman and she feels more intoxicated more rapidly. Some evidence suggests that women reach higher peak alcohol concentrations more rapidly than men, but metabolize the alcohol more slowly and so feel the effects of alcohol for longer.

Many researchers believe there is also some hormonal factor in the body's ability to cope with alcohol. Certainly some experiments have shown that women reach particularly high peak blood-alcohol concentrations and rapid absorption during the mid-cycle ovulation and just before menstruation which seems to corroborate this. It has also been shown that women on the pill are slower to break down alcohol – and should accordingly be more careful when drinking and driving. A hormonal link also helps explain why some women feel that their head for drink seems to fluctuate considerably, and why some women have exceptional reactions to drink during and just after pregnancy when the body is subject to exceptional hormone shifts.

What has been firmly established, however, is that the female body is particularly susceptible to damage wrought by alcohol. Because alcohol is more concentrated in our body tissues, it seems logical that it will damage our tissues more quickly than a comparable amount of alcohol would in a male body. Female livers appear to be especially vulnerable. Liver damage is the most common medical harm wrought by alcohol, but some research shows that whereas a consumption of more than ten drinks a day usually precedes the development of cirrhosis in a man, women need hardly more than six drinks a day before greatly increasing their cirrhosis risk – and there is even some risk at between two and three drinks a day for women.

These research conclusions have to be interpreted in the light of the fact that almost all of them depend on people telling the truth about how much they drink. Researchers usually have to rely on verbal testimony rather than regular long-term blood-alcohol measures to decide how much the interviewee drinks. It is possible, since heavy drinking is a much less socially acceptable trait in women than men in some social groups, that some women are more coy than men about confessing to their true alcohol intake. If so, the cirrhotic woman who said she only drank three drinks a week might actually drink a good deal more.

There is quite objective evidence, however, that once a female liver is damaged, that damage is much more difficult to reverse than damage to a male liver. It all seems very unfair, but perhaps this is nature's way of trying to keep the child-nurturers of the species sober.

A Head for Drink – Does It Exist?

We are all familiar with the phenomenon that some people seem to hold their drink better than others. Some of the reasons why women are more likely to be affected by alcohol than men, and how physical build plays a part in tolerance of alcohol in both sexes, are outlined above. The smaller you are, and the more spare fat you have, the more dramatic will be the effects of a given dose of alcohol.

There are other physical explanations. Anyone who has had surgery on their digestive system, particularly on the stomach or small intestine, finds that alcohol affects them very markedly soon after it is drunk because it passes into the system so rapidly. Excessive consumption of alcohol may chronically inflame the stomach lining and will aggravate (although not cause) ulcers. If a peptic ulcer, or anything else, is treated with a partial gastrectomy, then any alcohol will have an exaggerated effect.

Since the variation in our differing capacities to tolerate alcohol cannot be explained simply by physiological differences, there is a widely held theory that genetics play a part in determining our reaction to alcohol, perhaps specifically by governing the effectiveness of our ADH enzymes. Many of us will have observed some hard-drinking dynasties in our time, as well as some notably weak-headed families. The theory is supported by those population groups, notably in the Orient, with a high proportion of members who react adversely to alcohol, most specifically by facial flushing. One study established that whereas 2-3 per cent of Occidentals react to alcohol by flushing, the proportion among Orientals is 70-80 per cent. (This flushing does not necessarily act as a deterrent, however: North American Indians have a high incidence of both flushing and alcohol abuse.)

The nature of the way in which we metabolize alcohol suggests a further possible specific reason why our alcohol tolerance varies so much. Under the action of the ADH enzyme, alcohol is converted into the more toxic substance acetaldehyde. At high levels, acetaldehyde increases blood pressure, sets the heart beating faster, encourages nausea, flushing and breathing difficulties – in short, brings on some of the less pleasant side-effects of over-indulgence. Luckily, most of us have plentiful supplies of another enzyme, acetaldehyde dehydrogenase, which rapidly converts the toxic acetaldehyde into harmless acetate, which is itself rapidly (and simplistically) converted into carbon dioxide and water by further enzymes. (Antabuse, a drug designed to stop people drinking, works by competing for acetaldehyde dehydrogenase.)

Because all this takes place so fast, most of us do not experience the nasty side-effects of having acetaldehyde in our bodies. It seems highly possible, however, that those who react badly to alcohol have a much slower rate of acetaldehyde breakdown, and perhaps less acetaldehyde dehydrogenase. Certainly one study found that those with a history of alcohol problems had notably higher levels of acetaldehyde than normal drinkers.

It may well be, too, that the all-too-well-documented ravages of alcohol on the body are caused, at least in part, by the much more toxic acetaldehyde that is the natural result of ADH's action on any alcoholic intake. This aspect of alcohol research, of more interest to the social drinker than the problem drinker, has not attracted the interest and funds that projects which involve the more serious aspects of alcohol abuse and the community have, and so we may have to wait some time for more detailed knowledge of why some of us feel drunker than others.

Some psychologists also suggest that personality plays a part in our response to alcohol. Dr Michael Gossop of Maudsley Hospital's Drug Dependence Clinical Research and Treatment Unit in London is convinced that "introverts seem to be comparatively resistant to the effects of alcohol, whereas extraverts succumb to its intoxicating influence much more readily. The opposite is true of stimulant drugs like amphetamine or caffeine. At most parties, the extraverted behaviour of the guests can be directly linked to the amount of drink that has been consumed. Drunkenness is a chemical equivalent of extreme extraversion." According to Dr Gossop, it is the introverts who find their behaviour changes most dramatically under the influence of stimulants, whereas the extravert drinker is relatively unmoved.

Many of those who have used several psychoactive drugs (and most of us have used at least alcohol and caffeine) have observed that individuals have different preferences in drugs, as in anything else we consume. Indeed, there is a theory that for every personality there is a drug to which that personality would most readily respond. The introvert/extravert distinction helps to explain this, although an individual's reaction to alcohol also varies with both age and situation.

Drinking and Ageing

Age does seem to take its toll on our ability to take alcohol. This may be partly because, like all our bodily functions, our metabolizing of alcohol simply becomes less efficient. The structure of our bodies also changes and many of us increase our ratio of subcutaneous fat, which may concentrate the alcohol in our blood.

Certainly many people who have drunk heavily in their youth find that in middle age they feel drunk after much less alcohol (unless they have a strong psychological motivation for compensating for this physical phenomenon). As soon as we start drinking we develop a tolerance for alcohol. Heavy drinkers tend to develop a tolerance for a great deal of alcohol and some, up to a certain point in their lives, need more and more to feel drunk, but a sudden reduction in this tolerance may signal severe damage to the liver, notoriously difficult for the sufferer to identify. Heavy drinking tends to inflame and enlarge the liver, markedly and sometimes seriously straining the portal system which feeds the liver from the stomach and small intestine, but also reduces the drinker's tolerance to alcohol in a noticeable but as yet ill-understood way.

It is widely believed that stress and fatigue play a major part in determining our response to alcohol, and that therefore the young drinker, probably at the least stressful point in his life – as well as probably enjoying the lowest proportion of fat in his body – is most easily able to cope with large intakes of alcohol. This may also help to explain our apparent fluctuation in ability to tolerate alcohol, and why some women experience a sudden change in this respect just after childbearing.

Nutrition is thought to play an important part in warding off the ill-effects of alcohol. This may be a factor in our generally more feeble state vis-à-vis strong drink as we age. Certainly the very old and the very young are the two most susceptible age groups.

How Alcohol Can Be Tamed

Our knowledge of how alcohol works on us is incomplete, but good enough to suggest some very specific ways in which the effects of a given amount of alcohol can be muted.

The most obvious is one of the most often ignored. Food, and in particular carbohydrates and fatty foods, can make the most dramatic impact on the rate and peak of intoxication. Those who drink to take an express train to oblivion should ensure that they drink on an empty stomach. The absorption of the alcohol into the blood will proceed rapidly and unimpeded (unless it is taken as neat spirits – see page 68), and will probably reach the highest possible peak in blood-alcohol level from that amount of alcohol quite quickly. If, on the other hand, there is food in the digestive system, the alcohol has to take its turn with the masticated food to reach the wall of the stomach, and more particularly the first two feet of small intestine leading from it, where most alcohol is absorbed. This, of course, slows down the absorption considerably and usually means that the blood-alcohol concentration peaks at a lower level, resulting in less violent effects of intoxication. Because fats delay the digestive process and slow the emptying of the stomach into the small intestine, fatty foods, however unfashionable some of them may be on other criteria, are particularly effective at slowing alcohol absorption. Hence the advice to drink a glass of whole milk before going boozing.

Those of us who enjoy the gentler effects of alcohol would therefore be well advised to avoid drinking on an empty stomach, to try to nibble something whenever we drink, preferably before and preferably something fatty or oily, and to try to keep eating while we drink. The cocktail snack really does have a medical raison d'être, it would seem. This is unwelcome advice to those who are watching their weight, of course, and the choice between a slim silhouette and a healthy liver is a difficult one for many in these diet-conscious times. (It may well help explain why professional wine tastings, which usually take place in late morning, seem so much more intoxicating even to quite diligent spitters than they should.)

It is only very recently that it has been possible to do much eating in Britain's drinking centres, at least in our 75,000 pubs and hotels, which means that far too many Britons have learnt culturally to separate their eating and drinking activities. Our social habits and the advertisers reinforce the idea that spirits, beer and even cider are for drinking without food – even though the last two, like that other ferment, wine, make excellent lubricants for food. There would probably be much less extreme drunkenness in public places if there were better provision of edible brakes on the alcohol absorption process, but doubtless Britain's drinkers will continue to ignore the good that concurrent eating could do them, for reasons of (misguided?) economy and in response to our current reluctance to eat a morsel more than pure greed dictates.

There are other ways of mitigating alcohol's effects, slightly less theoretical "amethystic agents" than Hoffmann-LaRoche's RO15-4513. The jury is out and not looking convinced about either high doses of vitamin C or caffeine. The sobering-up qualities of a cup of black coffee after a bibulous meal are probably considerably more dubious than the efficacy of a cup of milky coffee as a pre-prandial brake on the effects of alcohol.

Scientists looking for ways of usefully speeding up the process of breaking down alcohol, thereby reducing intoxication faster (and making diagnosis of head injury easier in accidents, for example), have been drawn to fructose, the fruit-sugar laevulose that is commercially available at pharmacies and some health-food shops. It works effectively as an accelerator of alcohol metabolism, and there are those in the pharmaceutical industry who dose themselves if planning to drive after drinking. Unfortunately, however, it has to be taken in such high doses that it can induce stomach cramps and diarrhoea – a price that many will feel hardly inclined to pay.

Temperature also plays a part, and a rather deceptive one to the drinker. As alcohol rushes into the blood, it dilates the blood vessels which increases the flow of blood just below the skin, causing the flush that is such a familiar sign of indulgence. This makes us feel as though we are being warmed by the alcohol when, in fact, the alcohol is merely creaming off some of our deep body heat, exposing it to the cooler air on our skin and actually effectively cooling us down. The St Bernard dog's traditional barrel of brandy may be ill-advised, and it would certainly be unwise for elderly people on the brink of hypothermia to console themselves with alcohol.

The Importance of Mood

Most regular drinkers are familiar with the puzzling phenomenon that when one is in the mood, one sip can have a more intoxicating effect than three drinks when one is not. As outlined at the beginning of this chapter, we behave under the influence as we feel we should. In our culture we are generally encouraged to be sociable and animated when under the influence, but particularly so when we are at a party, a celebration or in a setting, such as a pub, which we associate with inebriated behaviour.

Several experiments have even shown that drinkers who were given nonalcoholic drinks, but drank them believing they were alcoholic, behaved in a way indistinguishable from intoxication. And many of us have experienced the sensation of feeling, when in particularly high spirits, immediately inebriated after just one sip of strong drink – a medical impossibility. This is presumably because we associate the effects of alcohol with its smell and taste, so that once we have learnt the experience of inebriation we no longer have to wait for its medical course to be run, which should take about half an hour, although less on an empty stomach.

Are Some Alcoholic Drinks More Dangerous Than Others?

Much as I love wine, I have to admit that there is absolutely no medical difference between the alcohol contained in wine and that contained in, say, vodka or strong lager. Ethyl alcohol is ethanol is ethyl alcohol.

In our culture, however, wine is the alcoholic drink most often drunk with food. According to Mintel market research in 1985, less than 20 per cent of all wine drunk in this country is drunk without a meal, whereas hardly ten per cent of all spirits drunk are drunk with a meal. The researchers did not even enquire how much beer was drunk with food. This makes wine the drink enjoyed most sensibly.

As the eminent alcohol-studies academic Robin Room of Berkeley, California, put it to me, "Wine shines in the context of social problems with its strong associations with middle-class behaviour, but it certainly does not shine when correlated with cirrhosis rates." That is to say that there is some evidence that wine drinking is associated with increased risk of chronic liver disease, although this may simply be because wine happens to be the cheapest form of alcohol in those countries such as France, Italy and Portugal where alcohol consumption and cirrhosis mortality are particularly high. Certainly France's highest cirrhosis rate is in its non-wine-drinking northwestern corner, and the Hungarians with their exceptionally high cirrhosis mortality rate are more notable drinkers of spirits than wine. And cirrhosis mortality in the United States fell by 34 per cent between 1974 and 1985, a period during which the nation turned from hard liquor to wine.

Some people find that they react badly to either red or white wine, but this is independent of the wine's alcohol content. There are more low-alcohol whites than reds, and more high-alcohol reds than whites, but the average red wine is no stronger than the average white. Sulphur dioxide, the most common preservative in winemaking and to which some asthmatics react particularly badly, is usually highest in sweet and white wines.

As for other inherent medical differences between the different forms of alcohol, beer is much better than wines or spirits for those with a folate deficiency, a problem in those whose drinking has taken such a hold that they are poorly nourished from other sources. In other words, severe alcohol abusers who drank only beer would alleviate this particular one of their many likely problems because beer contains some folic acid, whereas wines and spirits do not. However, some correlation between beer drinking and cancer of the colon or rectum has been established, and cancer of the oesophagus, which seems closely linked to alcohol intake – although not as closely as to smoking – seems closely associated with intake of spirits in particular. But these are small statistical relationships rather than alarming wholesale predispositions.

Of much more widespread value to social drinkers is the knowledge that the body absorbs alcohol most rapidly if it is taken in a drink of between 15 and 30 per cent alcohol. This explains why the supposedly genteel glass of sherry or port (about 18 per cent alcohol) can have such a dramatic effect. It is also worth noting that if a standard full-strength 40 per cent spirit is diluted with about the same volume of nonalcoholic mixer, then its effects will be most dramatically immediate. (This may explain why some habitual drinkers are so particular about exactly the proportions in which their drinks are mixed.)

Below 15 per cent, the strength of most table wines and all beers, the rate of absorption is much more gradual and the process of inebriation much gentler. It also makes sense to take alcohol in a dilute form, since alcohol itself is a diuretic and additional fluids are needed to stop the unpleasant sensation of dehydration so closely associated with hangovers.

If alcohol is taken in a form stronger than about 30 per cent, as neat whisky or brandy, for instance, the stomach lining is irritated by this concentration of alcohol and secretes a mucus which lines the stomach wall and delays absorption. This delay may be exaggerated by an exit valve in the stomach which is thought to close up reflexively under the action of high-strength alcoholic drinks, which is why the intoxication process of strong spirits can be deceptively delayed. A post-prandial brandy may thus have an even more dramatic effect on a Breathalyzer than the same amount of alcohol absorbed much more rapidly as, say, port. There is also some evidence that carbon dioxide encourages this valve to open, which may explain why champagne, and spirits diluted with fizzy mixers, seem to have a more rapid effect than still drinks of the same strength. The sugar content of sweet drinks, on the other hand, helps to delay alcohol absorption.

The alcoholic strengths of the various drinks most commonly drunk in this country are spelt out in Chapter Seven, What Is a Drink Anyway?. It is now, at last, mandatory to specify the strength of all alcoholic drinks in Europe, but for wine at least the new obligatory system is actually less accurate than the old voluntary one. The new wine system allows producers to specify alcoholic strength to the nearest 0.5 per cent, rounding either up or down. They have, on top of that, a tolerance of plus or minus 0.5 per cent, and a further 0.3 per cent tolerance for vintage-dated wines. So someone bottling a vintage-dated wine that is, in fact, say, 11.9 per cent alcohol, could now label it 10.7, or a deceptive tenth less potent than it really is.

The alcoholic strengths of all spirits must be spelt out on the label, in the same percentage-by-volume system as wines, although bottles labelled before 1982 may still be marked with the old British proof system (40% = 70° UK proof = 80° US proof).

It is in beers and ciders that the system has perhaps been most confusing, since the strongest of them can be three times the strength of the weakest, and many times stronger than the low-alcohol beers. When alcoholic strength is specified for a beer it has been given in original gravity, for instance 1037 for a lager, which roughly (although by no means always) translates into an alcoholic strength of 3.7 per cent. From 1988, European law requires all beers to be labelled with their alcoholic strength in percentage by volume, so it will be much easier for beer drinkers to regulate (and, presumably, maximize) their alcoholic intake. It is worth bearing in mind that, like the wine bottlers, the brewers have been allowed a fair amount of leeway in the alcoholic strength specified – and that some brewers actually change the strength of their brew, sometimes according to the season. One famous beer is supposed to be brewed at a notably lower strength for summer drinking. It pays to study the small print.

The Brewers' Society has records of the average strength of beers brewed in this country since the turn of the century. These show how British brews have declined considerably in strength, with marked dips during the two World Wars, since the bibulous end of the Victorian era. At the turn of the century it was on average nearly 5.5 per cent, whereas in 1986 it was just under 3.8 per cent – although this average was the highest since the beginning of World War II, presumably because of the increasing popularity of high-strength lagers.

Some argue that it would be particularly helpful if drinks such as cans of beer were marked with the number of units of alcohol they contain, but there is another factor in how different drinks affect us: their congeners content. These are discussed later in this chapter in relation to one of life's shorter-term insults to the drinker, the hangover.

A Realist's View of the Damage

This is the nastiest, but perhaps the most important, part of this book. Since 1986 we drinkers have been assailed by snippets of somewhat gruesome information about the predations of alcohol. Most of these have emanated from a small, concerned sector of the medical profession, which quite rightly wants to draw government's attention to the fact that it may be spending too much on fighting heroin abuse and not enough on alcohol problems. The scarier aspects of the facts have been disseminated in various media, usually without much analysis or examination of context. The aim of this section is to attempt a dispassionate look at the evidence so far as it affects the social drinker: someone who enjoys drinking occasionally or regularly but whose life does not revolve around it.

The most logical way of doing this is to examine each risk associated with drinking. There is, of course, a spectrum of social problems associated with excessive alcohol consumption – not just the harmful effects on the community of excessive drinking, but the specific effects on the family, work and personal behaviour of an individual. These need little spelling out here. We are, in addition, more liable to injury and accidents of any sort when intoxicated. Probably the most common alcohol-related cause of death, the traffic accidents that result from drunken driving, are examined in Chapter Eleven, The Quiet Massacre.

This section, on the other hand, is concerned with the specifically medical evidence against long-term use of alcohol, with the potential risk areas examined in what is a very approximate descending order of likelihood. Because it is such a "hot" issue, alcohol and pregnancy are examined in detail in a separate section in this chapter. But first, the importance of Alcohol, the Killer, should be examined.

How Big a Killer?

Among the many issues hotly contended between those campaigning "anti" and "for" alcohol, by far the most controversial is a single statistic: the number of Britons who die as a result of alcohol. It is well established, for example, that 100,000 people a year die prematurely as a result of smoking. Exactly 47 registered opiate addicts (from a total of around 6,000) died in 1985. Much more nebulous is the link between drinking and death.

The last detailed figures for alcohol-related deaths given in Parliament were those in 1983. In England and Wales, just over 2,000 people died of chronic liver disease and cirrhosis. But there are many nonalcohol-related causes of cirrhosis, including viral hepatitis and chronic heart disease, and it is not clear exactly how many of these deaths were alcohol-related. Alcohol was officially acknowledged to have played any part in fewer than 900 of them – although there is evidence that doctors have, until recently, been substantially underreporting the role of alcohol. Analysis of death certificates showed there were also 384 accidental deaths (other than road accidents) in which alcohol was mentioned, 104 deaths through "non-dependent abuse of alcohol", 99 through alcohol dependency and two people who simply drank themselves to death (as compared with the 304 Swedish deaths so notified in 1984, on a population base only that of London).

Add to this the debated figure for our alcohol-related deaths on the road of between 1,000 and 1,700, and the total number of deaths in which alcohol is *known* to have played a principal part is still only about 5,000 (although the Royal College of General Practitioners' 1986 report managed to bulk this figure up to a hotly contested 40,000).

This is still 5,000 too many, and almost certainly a serious underestimate. Indeed, the latest figures for cirrhosis and liver-disease mortality, for 1985, show 2,582 deaths, with those of women accounting for 46 per cent. And there are doubtless thousands of deaths in which alcohol was a factor. But it is important to stress that alcohol does not appear to be a major national killer compared to the 287,054 deaths in 1985 through diseases of the circulatory system (chiefly heart attacks, to which heavy drinkers are admittedly more prone), the 139,822 through cancers of various sorts and the 64,607 deaths from diseases of the respiratory system.

If one calculates the annual death rate as a proportion of the total number of users, alcohol is very much less serious a killer than, say, tobacco or heroin. If 100,000 smokers out of 17.5 million die each year, the tobacco mortality rate is about 571 deaths in every 100,000 users. The 1985 figure of 47 deaths of opiate addicts suggests a heroin mortality rate of 783 deaths in every 100,000 users – although the tiny statistical base and the complex web of secrecy and bureaucracy make it difficult to get a true picture of heroin use. Even if 10,000 drinkers out of the national total of about 40 million were to die each year directly from alcohol-related causes – and this is twice as many as have been proved – the alcohol mortality rate would still be only about 25 deaths in every 100,000 drinkers.

This is not to say that alcohol is not a potentially dangerous drug. In certain settings it can be an instrument of grave social harm, breaking up families and causing incalculable human misery. It is a major hazard at work, responsible for thousands of man-hours of lost productivity, and for a wide range of diseases and disabilities which are painful, sometimes fatal, and cost the country a great deal of money. The most common are examined below.

Liver

In view of the way we absorb alcohol, it is hardly surprising that it does most notable damage to the liver. The average healthy male liver seems to be able to metabolize about 80 grams of alcohol, or ten units, in any 24 hours – the average female liver perhaps only half that. However, there is a great deal of individual variation, and any liver that is subjected to regular high doses may never manage to return to normal and detoxify itself. This is why doctors recommend two or three days' total abstinence each week.

As the enzymes get to work and convert alcohol eventually to water and carbon dioxide, fat rapidly builds up in the blood. Alcohol intake may reach such a pitch that this fat is deposited, most damagingly in the liver (but also in the heart muscle), causing fatty liver, the first sign of liver damage and common in heavy drinkers, even though there are few perceptible symptoms. If excessive consumption continues, then alcoholic hepatitis, an inflammation of the liver, may also set in. Fatty liver and the early stages of alcoholic hepatitis are reversible, and the fat in the tender, enlarged liver will be re-absorbed after two or three months' abstinence or at least dramatically reduced drinking. Large doses of the B vitamins are also usually prescribed to make up for recent nutritional deficiencies, for a damaged liver ceases to function efficiently as a processor of what we eat. In just over half of all cases of alcoholic hepatitis, the condition persists unchanged for several years. In about ten per cent of cases it heals despite continued alcohol abuse.

But in some drinkers and, the signs are, particularly in women, such a condition may be irreversible. Certainly if the drinker continues to drink heavily, in probably between ten and 30 per cent of those who develop fatty liver the liver becomes increasingly enlarged, inflamed, knobbly and irrevers-ibly damaged. Alcoholic cirrhosis may lead to liver failure and death as this vital organ simply becomes more diseased and unable to do its complex and essential work. Older bodies find it more difficult to grow healthy new liver tissue to replace the old damaged tissue during the period of abstinence that is needed after alcoholic cirrhosis has been diagnosed.

There is a better chance of surviving alcoholic cirrhosis than other forms of cirrhosis. There is no cure, but abstention has been shown to halt its spread. One study found that 69 per cent of those who abstained after having a positive alcoholic cirrhosis diagnosis were alive five years after, compared with only 34 per cent of those who continued to drink.

Alcoholic cirrhosis may also lead to liver cancer. About a third of all deaths from alcoholic cirrhosis – that is, several hundred a year – result from primary liver-cell cancer.

These gloomy facts are sufficient to make most drinkers anxious for more information about the state of their own livers, but liver damage is exasperatingly difficult to diagnose correctly. Many drinkers with fatty livers feel no symptoms at all. Some may develop further problems; others not. Even laboratory liver-function tests are notoriously unreliable. Some show signs of severe liver failure long before the cirrhosis stage, whereas some cirrhotic livers show remarkably few abnormalities.

Different people vary as much in their predisposition to liver damage as in their ability to cope with alcohol's intoxicating effects on the nervous system. It is by no means certain that these two are related. All that is certain is the grim truth that any given individual increases his susceptibility to liver damage when he increases his alcohol intake, and that past a certain average daily intake the risk becomes quite severe. There have been many studies correlating liver damage with (reported) alcoholic intake, and these form one of the primary bases for the medical Royal Colleges' recommended "safe limits" (see Chapter Seven, How Much Is Enough?).

These rough statistical pictures of widely varying medical realities suggest that the point at which the risk of some liver damage starts to increase sharply is at about five units of alcohol a day for men and two and a half for women. Establishing the base line for such a common activity as drinking is very difficult, of course. One of the most detailed studies was conducted in the French département of Calvados, where the researchers had such difficulty in finding adults who drank less than ten grams of alcohol a day that the category of lowest consumption had to be set at 0-19 grams, or up to two and a half drinks daily.

Without any wish to encourage excessive consumption, it is only fair to underline the comparative rarity of cirrhosis mortality in Britain: fewer than six deaths a year in every 100,000 people, most of the 100,000 being drinkers. And to quote from the Royal College of Physicians on the intermediary stage between fatty liver and cirrhosis in their 1987 report, *A Great and Growing Evil*: "Alcoholic hepatitis develops in only a proportion of heavy drinkers even after decades of drinking."

Professor R. E. Kendell of Edinburgh was even more bullish when delivering the first Benno Pollak Lecture, on *Drinking Sensibly*, at the Institute of Psychiatry in London in 1987. Concluding his remarks on how alcohol affects the individual, he said: "There is probably no level of drinking, certainly no level of lifelong daily drinking, which is wholly free of risk. This does not mean, however, that we should all become abstainers, or urge our fellow countrymen to do so. Even if, in reality, regularly drinking, say, ten grams of alcohol a day were associated with a doubling of the risk of developing cirrhosis over a lifetime, that is not very serious. In the absence of alcohol, cirrhosis is a comparatively rare disease, so most people would probably be prepared to contemplate a doubling of that risk with equanimity."

But it has been demonstrated that those most at risk are women, those of either sex whose body tissues contain certain identifiable antigens (notably B8 or DR3, for the medically well versed) and even, according to some studies, members of some ethnic groups. American research suggests that black populations are susceptible to liver damage at much lower levels of intake than white. Simplistically, therefore, it would seem that white males, the population subgroup that has had the longest drinking experience, have evolved better bodily defences against the ravages of alcohol than women and blacks, who are relative newcomers to the demon drink.

Heart and Blood Pressure

The good news for drinkers, as detailed in Chapter Two, is that there is considerable evidence, from more than 15 different sources, that moderate consumption of alcohol can lessen the risk of the nation's biggest killer, coronary heart disease. On the other hand, alcohol can deposit fat in the heart muscle, which predisposes heavy drinkers to heart attacks. Those with failing heart muscle or cardiomyopathy are advised not to drink. Binge drinking can precipitate unusual syncopations in the heartbeat, but these do not (necessarily) presage chronic heart disease.

It has been established recently, however, that alcohol is a common cause of high blood pressure, or hypertension. There is a direct linear relationship between alcohol consumption and blood pressure quite independent of age, weight, ethnic origin, social class, reported salt intake and smoking habits. The Royal College of General Practioners' 1986 report on alcohol observed: "Excess alcohol intake is probably the most common identifiable cause of hypertension", and their Physician colleagues reported the next year: "All hypertensive patients should be screened for alcohol excess because, with abstinence, blood pressure settles".

The J-shaped curve correlating the incidence of heart attacks with alcohol consumption (see page 26) is, interestingly, mirrored in many researchers' correlations between blood pressure and drinking habits. It seems that, on average, those who consume two drinks a day have a slightly lower blood pressure than complete teetotallers, although past this level of intake the average blood pressure rapidly increases. Raised blood pressure is exceptionally high in heavy drinkers, but they can lower it to normal levels by drinking less. Strokes are closely related to high blood pressure, and indeed heavy alcohol consumption can double, some think treble, the incidence of fatal strokes. A single real bender can also precipitate a stroke in those with raised blood pressure.

It would seem to follow, therefore, that those who are predisposed to hypertension are particularly at risk from heavy drinking. The increase in blood pressure usually follows immediately the intake of alcohol and persists until the blood-alcohol level falls, although the exact mechanism which explains this phenomenon is not yet understood.

It also follows that many strokes would be avoided by better monitoring and correlating of blood pressure and alcohol intake. The Royal College of Physicians estimates that alcohol accounts for the raised blood pressure in ten to 15 per cent of patients with hypertension, which is about ten per cent of the population in the 30-60 age bracket, or 250,000 to 375,000 individuals. If each of these individuals lowered alcohol intake to "safe" levels, many thousands of strokes might be avoided.

Brain and Nervous System

Alcohol is a toxic substance and affects all tissues of the body. After the liver, the brain appears to be the most susceptible – which should not surprise any drinker, to whom the impact of alcohol on the brain is so obvious. The social drinker should experience only the effects on the brain of a large dose of alcohol on a single occasion, which include torpor and memory loss or "blackout". The grim catalogue of withdrawal symptoms in severely dependent long-term drinkers, however, includes "the shakes", or the tremor that appears between 12 and 24 hours after the last drink and is most obvious in the upper limbs. Hallucinations may also develop but, despite the common currency of the term "DTS", true delirium tremens is a comparatively rare and very specific syndrome, developing two to five days after a chronic drinker stops drinking. With true DT, the panic, hallucinations and extreme overactivity can be severe. In older people and those with other medical complications, DTS can even be fatal.

Two of the more notable conditions associated, usually together, with very prolonged alcohol abuse, Wernicke's encephalopathy and Korsakoff's syndrome (ripe candidates for a Tom Stoppard dramatization, surely), affect the nervous system and in particular the eyes. The first, a sort of alcoholic delirium observable in cases of severe abuse, can be effectively treated with injections of thiamine or vitamin B_1, again showing how important the relationship is between nutrition and alcohol consumption. Even if alcohol abusers do not have an abnormal diet – and many of them do – they abuse their absorption system for various nutrients, demonstrating another way in which excessive alcohol consumption can harm the body.

These are all extreme instances of damage to the brain and nervous system due to alcohol, as is the fact – recently proved by physical examination in the forensic laboratories of Perth in Western Australia – that specific parts of the brain, notably the superior frontal cortex, are observably damaged in alcoholics. The researchers' findings were reported in the *British Medical Journal* under the cheerful title: *Are we drinking our neurones away?* Some recent Australian research also suggests that even heavy social drinkers may suffer brain shrinkage as a result of their alcohol intake. X-rays certainly suggest this in problem drinkers, those who have been abusing alcohol for at least five years. It may even help to explain, in part, why problem drinkers find it so difficult to control their drinking; that bit of the brain that affects controls on behaviour may be damaged.

Three months' abstinence will usually end the confusions and problems with concentration experienced as a result of this brain shrinkage, although brain tissue is bad at regenerating itself and renewed vigour in what is left is the best that can be hoped for.

It may be that individuals' variation in their susceptibility to alcohol-related brain damage is linked to the activity of their thiamine-dependent enzyme transketolase. It is tempting, but almost certainly too simplistic, to infer that thiamine could save the neurones of heavy social drinkers. The Royal College of Physicians' 1987 report made the stimulating point that: "The optimal form of nutritional therapy and its potential benefit at early stages of alcohol damage remains to be documented".

Gut

Alcohol is a carcinogen, not as powerful a one as nicotine perhaps, but all those parts of the body that come into direct contact with alcohol in its unprocessed form may therefore develop cancers. This applies particularly to the mouth, the oesophagus or gullet, and the passage between them, the pharynx. Heavy alcohol consumption increases the risk of cancer of the larynx, which connects the pharynx to the lungs, four times; of the pharynx and mouth (excluding the lip, which rarely comes into direct contact with alcohol) three times; and the risk of cancer of the oesophagus (the most common of these risks, although only the ninth most common cancer in men and less common in women) is doubled. There is also some slightly shakier evidence that heavy drinking is associated with a high risk of cancer of the colon and rectum.

All these cancers are relatively rare, but they are some of the few cancers that are becoming slowly more common. Cancer of the oesophagus is usually fatal, and its incidence in Europe is highest in France. Elsewhere there seems to be a correlation between a nation's average alcoholic intake and the rate of cancer of the oesophagus, although religious groups in high-rate areas who abstain are much less prone to it.

There is no evidence to suggest that any particular form of alcohol affects the likely oesophageal cancer rate apart from some slight statistical connections with spirits consumption, but drinking more than ten alcohol units of any sort a day seems to increase the risk eighteenfold, from one in 140 for men and one in 330 for women.

Alcohol exacerbates gastric or duodenal ulcers and can cause acute gastritis, an inflammation of the stomach lining. A few days' abstention should cure this inflammation. Alcohol is also seriously implicated as a cause of pancreatitis, or inflammation of the pancreas, in at least half of all cases. There is evidence that the more alcohol that is consumed daily, the greater the risk of this painful and sometimes fatal disorder. Long-term heavy drinking is the usual precursor: about 11 years for women and 17 for men.

Gout – a Footnote

The medical profession's views on the supposed link between alcohol and gout may be deduced from the fact that the latest catalogue of medical disasters that the demon drink may entail, the Royal College of Physicians' *A Great and Growing Evil*, does not even mention it. Nor did its counterpart from the Royal College of General Practitioners. Gout is a painful arthritic condition of the joints which results from a defect in our metabolism of uric acid. Uric acid is naturally present in the body, but if its metabolism fails its salts, the urates, accumulate in the bloodstream and joints. The level of uric acid in the blood increases with heavy alcohol consumption. Overindulgence does not therefore cause gout but, in those individuals with a faulty uric acid metabolism, it will exacerbate it.

Alcohol and Men

Few male drinkers need Shakespeare, or medical science, to tell them that alcohol "provokes the desire but takes away the performance", as the Porter complained to Macduff in Macbeth. Brewer's droop is a phenomenon familiar enough to have been fully absorbed into common folklore and into the complex dances of adult sexual behaviour. In fact, so familiar is the phenomenon that there has been remarkably little research into the mechanisms behind it. What has attracted space in the medical journals, however, and subsequent sensationalism in the tabloids, is some recent research results that strike at some of man's most atavistic fears: that heavy drinking can effect long-term damage to the sexual organs and sex drive.

Daily titillators such as the *Sun* eventually published the juicier snippets from a complex research paper by Dr Marsha Morgan, of London's Royal Free Hospital, which had been published in 1982. The translation had been provided five years later by the Royal College of Physicians in their chapter on alcohol abuse and the sexual function: "Men complain of loss of libido and potency and may develop shrinking of the testes, a reduction in the size of the penis, diminished or absent sperm formation, loss of sexual hair, and of scrotal wrinkling". Gold indeed for those digging for populist anti-alcohol evidence. Even in the post-hippie era, when in many social subgroups celibacy is stigma-free and even fashionable, to a high proportion of the male population one of the very few things for which the sacrifice of alcohol might not be too great is sex, or at least the ability to function sexually. (One 1981 research study found, however, that alcoholics with persistent sexual problems are likely to continue to abuse alcohol).

Long-term heavy drinking certainly has a toxic effect, quite independent of liver damage and nutritional deficiencies, on the testes and on the pituary gland that controls the body's hormones. Dr Morgan's research suggests that the body, for some reason, produces more of the female hormone oestrogen in heavy drinkers. This presumably accounts for the fact that some male alcohol abusers experience shrinkage of their sexual organs, and may even start to lose body hair and grow breasts – the ultimate insult to the hard-drinking male.

These hormonal and sexual problems seem to occur independently of liver damage, although male cirrhotics, those at the furthest end of the drinking spectrum, are more likely to report loss of libido and reduced sexual activity: 66-90 per cent, as opposed to 40-77 per cent of male alcoholics with minimal liver damage. Testicular shrinking was similarly reported in 10-50 per cent of the male alcoholics with healthy livers, but in 30-75 per cent of alcoholic cirrhotics.

One study of 17,000 male alcoholics found that eight per cent were impotent. It has since been shown, however, that abstinence (from alcohol) can combat impotence in alcohol abusers in 25 to 50 per cent of cases, although improvement is much more likely in drinkers whose hormonal disturbance has not yet started to wrinkle their winkles.

Perhaps the most useful and positive evidence concerning male sex and alcohol is recent research concerning the effect of drinking on male fertility. It seems that even quite moderate drinking can dramatically decrease the amount of sperm produced and its motility. In one study, 40 per cent of those attending a male infertility clinic were thought to have a low sperm count simply through drinking six units of alcohol (three pints of beer) a day. Three months' abstinence, sometimes as little as half that time, brought sperm counts back up to normal in half of the cases.

It would seem sensible, therefore, for any man whose intake is more than four units a day to cut down or even abstain for at least three months before he and his partner want to conceive. The reasons for moderation or abstention in potential mothers are given below, and it is certainly easier in practice for both members of a partnership to show restraint than one.

Another, more tenuous link between drinking and sex was reported in the *Journal* of the Royal College of Physicians late in 1987, which underlines the link between alcohol consumption and hormones. Hard on the heels of a study which found that butchers were more likely to have sons than daughters ("because they might have eaten more meat from animals given growth-promoting male hormones"), came the news that workers in the drinks industry are six to ten per cent more likely to produce daughters than sons. Perhaps because of the extra oestrogen floating around unchecked because of higher-than-average drinking?

Alcohol and Women

If this chapter could be said to have had a leitmotiv so far, it is that women are much more susceptible to alcohol-related damage than men. Every tissue of our bodies, it would seem, has notably fewer defences against the ravages of drink than those of men – perhaps because we have a much shorter history of drinking in any quantity. It is interesting, if tangential, to consider that drinking, as opposed to dainty and companionable sipping, has been an integral part of emancipation. And it has been only relatively recently that we have joined in this, one of man's favourite games.

The statistics confirm all this. The proportion of mothers with young children who drink had risen from 24 per cent in 1930 to 91 per cent in 1971. In 1981, a study of 15-16-year-old girls found only five per cent who were non-drinkers. We are also drinking more, although research indicates that heavier-drinking women tend to drink on more occasions than their less bibulous sisters, rather than have a greater intake each time they drink. (They are also more likely to be smokers, a combination with effects on the likelihood of oesophageal cancer and damage to the heart muscles.) As has already been pointed out (How Big a Killer?), the female cirrhosis mortality rate relative to the male rate is, worryingly and puzzlingly, higher in Britain than in any other well-documented country. In England and Wales, women are 85 per cent as likely to die of cirrhosis as men, whereas the proportions in the US and France are only 51 per cent and 41 per cent respectively. It is not as though British women drink so much more of the national total than their counterparts in the US and France. According to the most reliable estimates, women account for an estimated 25 per cent of the British total alcohol consumption, as opposed to 42.5 per cent of the American total and a third of the French total.

One of the most recent scare stories about alcohol has concerned a possible correlation between drinking and the incidence of breast cancer, the most common form of cancer in women, accounting for one in every five of all new female cancer cases in the UK in 1983, and one in every five female cancer deaths in 1985. In May 1987, the results of similar research projects at Harvard Medical School and the US National Cancer Institute at Bethesda, Maryland, were published. These seemed to show that women who drank between three and nine drinks a week are 30 per cent more likely to develop breast cancer than non-drinkers, while those who drank more than nine drinks a week increased their risk of breast cancer by 60 per cent.

This was important as the first evidence suggesting that light alcohol consumption was associated with substantial harm, although even a 60 per cent increased risk of a heavy drinker would translate into a probability of less than one in eight. The well-publicized and occasionally sensationalized link highlights the problems associated with interpretation of the majority of alcohol research. There is not only the problem of getting accurate figures on consumption through the self-reporting technique that is almost inevitably relied upon (although the Harvard study collected data on nearly 90,000 nurses before any diagnoses could colour the reporting). There is the usual difficulty with finding any biochemical explanation for a link between alcohol and the ill-effect, in this case breast cancer.

The researchers found that moderate drinking was on a par with most other factors that predispose a woman to breast cancer – a family history of the disease, high-fat diet, first pregnancy at 30+, obesity, early onset of menstruation and late onset of menopause – although the correlation between moderate drinking and breast cancer was quite independent of them. It could be that the moderate drinkers (who, even in the US, were presumably the majority of those studied) shared some other habit or physical predisposition not yet identified. The practical implication of this is that, for the moment, those to whom several of these risk factors already apply should be particularly careful to monitor and minimize their drinking.

There also seems to be a statistical link between drinking and those women who suffer from premenstrual tension and other gynaecological problems. Some women report that they use drink to stave off the pain associated with PMT (when the effects of alcohol are most pronounced), which may be a possible explanation for this link. There is clearly a need for more specific research here. There are suggestions, too, that chronic alcoholic women suffer from severe menstrual problems.

There is also a spectrum of particularly female psychological problems in which alcohol plays a part, notably an association between depression and alcohol-related problems, and a tendency for women with sexual problems to use alcohol as an escape from them or, in accordance with the images perpetrated by drinks advertisers, to somehow enhance sexual pleasure.

This could be counterproductive if it got out of hand, for there is also evidence of alcohol damage to the ovaries and pituary gland in heavy-drinking women corresponding to that in men described above, with some parallel "masculinization" of the body: the breasts, ovaries and external genitalia may start to shrink in chronic female drinkers, although this is much less well proven than the converse phenomenon in men.

It also seems likely, although it is so far quite unproven, that drinking in any quantity reduces female fertility. It is known that heavy alcoholic intake affects the reproductive efficiency of rodents, which are the only females researched so far. But there has been little research on women's drinking and conception since the early 1970s, when alcohol was cast as the scourge of the antenatal clinic and those wishing to conceive, at least in the US, the country with most medical research funds available, were expected to abstain.

Alcohol and Pregnancy

The issue about which there has been most publicity, and therefore a not inconsiderable amount of research, is alcohol and pregnancy. Ever since the belief that the "placental barrier" protected the unborn child against toxic substances in the mother's body was shattered, most notably in the tragic case of thalidomide-damaged children born in the 1960s, there has been research into the possible effects of toxins on the fetus. Alcohol was, of course, a likely candidate.

The Fetal Alcohol Syndrome (FAS) was christened in 1973 by three American researchers, Jones, Smith and Ulleland, who found some physiological similarities between eight children born to chronically alcoholic women who continued to drink throughout pregnancy. One of the children was born "while her mother was in an alcoholic stupor", two of the mothers suffered delirium tremens during pregnancy. Jones, Smith and Ulleland were not the first researchers to concern themselves with the impact of heavy drinking on the fetus. There has been understandable interest in the subject since biblical times. In 1968, a team of French researchers reported a similar pattern of abnormalities in 127 children born to chronic alcoholics (there was no differentiation between those of alcoholic mothers and those of alcoholic fathers). But by 1973 American attention was ready to be drawn to this aspect of alcohol abuse.

Here was physical evidence, albeit extremely specific and atypical, of alcohol's toxicity, and FAS could in some ways be said to have been the catalyst for the current explosion in research into the effects of alcohol.

The FAS abnormalities include general developmental delay, mental retardation, hyperactivity and short attention span (all characteristics which most anxious parents at one time or another identify in their offspring), together with certain physiological features. These show some variation from one group of researchers to another but most commonly include a short, upturned nose, receding forehead and chin, sunken nasal bridge and abnormal ears. Such babies are also light and small. They do not catch up with normal weights and measurements as healthy children do.

Since its emergence as a specific syndrome, researchers as far apart as Sweden, South Africa, Chile, France, West Germany, Northern Ireland, England and Scotland have diagnosed small numbers of children as exhibiting some combination of FAS symptoms. In Britain, the largest group identified as exhibiting FAS is a group of 40 identified in Glasgow between 1971 and 1981, with other smaller clusters in Liverpool and Belfast, and isolated occurences elsewhere which suggest a total British incidence of less than 1 in every 1,000 live births. The estimated incidence of FAS as calculated by researchers in their various other countries suggest that the highest incidence is in Sweden (1.6 in every 1,000) and Seattle (1.3 per 1,000).

It is important to stress now that such a disturbing concentration of birth defects as FAS has been found only in the children of serious abusers of alcohol (whose parents are typically socially deprived, poorly nourished and may well use tobacco and even illicit drugs to excess, too). But its naming and identification, however imprecise and rarely manifested, was enough to focus public attention on alcohol as a possible fetal toxin for women who drank even low to moderate quantities during pregnancy. There are few more emotive issues than women and babies, and the protective, almost proprietorial way in which society views the sanctity of the womb – surely the part of any human body which is thought most to belong in the public domain. The horror of a sin that a careless mother could inflict on an innocent baby nicely deflected national attention in America from the thousands of deaths on the highways for which drunk drivers were responsible. Now men could point the finger, too (and continued to do so until the research on drinking and male fertility emerged).

Such was the enthusiasm with which America tackled this new aspect of drug abuse that the official National Institute for Alcohol Abuse and Alcoholism, NIAAA, funded four major studies which were published between 1979 and 1981, the year in which the US Surgeon General advised all women to abstain completely throughout pregnancy.

Such effort and concern is, of course, entirely laudable. And, as some of Britain's impoverished medical researchers admit enviously, at least the Americans did something about a potential problem. But many observers wonder whether the official, if recent, American stance on alcohol and pregnancy is not unnecessarily stringent. One might expect, for example, a particularly high rate of birth defects and problems in pregnancy in countries such as France and Portugal, where the national intake of alcohol is particularly high. No research has been able to demonstrate this, however.

Another basic building block of evidence to support the theory that social drinking in pregnancy is dangerous is also missing. It is generally agreed that alcohol can do most harm in the crucial first three months of fetal development, when many women are unaware they are pregnant at all. In most European-based cultures, by far the heaviest drinking is done in December. It would thus be reasonable to expect any alcohol-fetal damage link to be apparent in a particularly high rate of obstetric difficulties and birth defects in October to December conceptions, and babies born between mid-July and mid-September. No such blip on the data exists. Indeed, such correlation as there has been of drinking habits in early pregnancy and the risk of birth defects shows that the mother has to drink at least ten units of alcohol (more than a bottle of wine or five pints of beer) on one occasion during the first three months to increase the risk of a damaged baby. It is interesting to note, even if of little probable scientific value, that many women find that alcohol, and coffee, seem unpalatable during pregnancy. Nature's way of saving all this research spending?

Many aspects of the American studies on which the Surgeon General's 1981 advice was based have been seriously questioned since. (In fact, so passionately do alcohol research specialists around the world feel about this emotive issue that police had to be called in at one American conference on alcohol and pregnancy.) Some doctors are even unconvinced about the existence of FAS as a clinically demonstrable syndrome at all. The climate in which much of the American research on all aspects of alcohol has been conducted has certainly been closer to a witch hunt than that of cool, objective scientific inquiry. Some unnecessary heat has probably also been generated by the fact that a number of alcohol researchers and workers on alcohol problems (not just in the US) are themselves reformed alcoholics or relatives of alcoholics.

The research does indicate fairly conclusively, and hardly surprisingly, that alcoholic women tend to have less successful pregnancies, resulting, if they reach full term, in babies with lower birth weights and a higher proportion of abnormalities. But Britain's expert on women, pregnancy and alcohol, Dr Moira Plant of the Alcohol Research Group in Edinburgh, argues in *Drinking and Pregnancy* for the *International Clinical Nutrition Review* that pregnancies of such an atypical group of women are influenced by a wide range of factors. She writes: "Recent well conducted prospective studies have clarified many issues, but the *causal* role of alcohol appears to be far less than some authors have suggested it might be. Women who drink very heavily run the risk of producing damaged babies. The difficulty in teasing out what causes the damage is immense. In general, women who drink heavily also smoke heavily and frequently use other drugs. Their diet is often poor and their general lifestyles unhealthy. It may be this whole lifestyle which determines the risk to the fetus and not one single factor."

Dr Plant continues: "There is little evidence to suggest that 'moderate' levels of maternal alcohol consumption during pregnancy have any harmful effects upon the unborn child....In the haste to protect the unborn child professionals have in the past run the risk of exaggerating in an attempt to convey their message. The general public now appears less willing to accept every pronouncement. Unnecessary stress, guilt and suffering may be caused by the simplistic message that alcohol per se even in small quantities is teratogenic."

This is not welcome news in Seattle, where America's most outspoken proponents of the dangers of FAS are based: the more scary the results they can emit, the more funds will be directed towards alcohol research and treatment in the US. Such sanguine advice is extremely welcome, however, to any woman who has had or is thinking of having, a child.

As has already been pointed out, though, realistic assessment of anyone's alcohol intake is extremely difficult, and a correct picture of a woman's drinking habits during pregnancy probably near-impossible – particularly if she is asked to report retrospectively on them just after having given birth to an abnormal baby.

Of more general importance is the not inconsiderable work to date attempting to correlate more normal social drinking with the likelihood of malformations, low birth weight, preterm delivery, still-birth, abruptio placenta, spontaneous abortion, birth defects and developmental problems. Even American medical research analysts Stein and Kline reported in the *American Journal of Public Health* in 1981 that all this research was "characterized by conspicuous and irksome inconsistencies".

Although no causal relationship or mechanisms have ever been proved in any of this research, some American researchers found statistical correlations between the form of the alcohol drunk during pregnancy and effects on the fetus. Specialists Kuzma and Sokol found that frequent "heavy beer drinking during pregnancy is related to decreased intra-uterine growth", whereas wine drinking was associated with *increased* birth weight (which might explain why French and Portuguese babies seem all right).

There have been understandable attempts to prove that there is a linear relationship between the amount drunk during pregnancy and the likelihood of behavioural problems in the resulting children. Close examination of the data, admittedly on small samples, reveals our old friend the J-shaped curve, i.e. the children of light drinkers, women who drank between one drink every three days and three drinks a day, did significantly better than those whose mothers drank an average of less than one drink every three days. A Rosett survey of 1,690 young, mainly low-income women in Boston in 1983 showed, in common with many other surveys, that heavy drinking was very commonly associated with heavy smoking and illicit drug use. The survey concluded: "We found adverse outcomes among offspring of women who drank heavily throughout pregnancy, but no effects in association with rare or moderate drinking" (which in the terms of this survey meant less than one and a half drinks daily, or never more than five on one occasion).

A Scottish survey between 1980 and 1982 interviewed 1,008 pregnant women when in the twelfth week of pregnancy and monitored their pregnancies and babies. The incidence of two or more alcohol-related abnormalities was dramatically increased in women who drank more than ten drinks on any one occasion during pregnancy, but it was almost impossible to predict which births and babies would be abnormal on the basis of the mother's drinking habits. In reality, doctors find themselves unable to explain a good 60 per cent of congenital abnormalities in any case, and the Scottish survey concluded that: "A number of factors appeared to have a stronger influence on pregnancy outcome than did alcohol consumption. These included previous obstetric history, maternal height and age, tobacco, medicine and illegal drug use and diet. This conclusion is compatible with those of other studies." Commenting in 1984 on the research to date in *Alcohol and the Fetus*, Rosett and Weiner concluded: "Many inconsistencies have been ignored, and data have been selectively cited and interpreted (Abel 1982). As a result, the danger of small amounts of alcohol has been exaggerated."

The official British medical line, as promulgated in the Royal Colleges' reports in 1987, is that pregnant women should drink moderately, no more than one or two drinks once or twice a week, and that alcohol probably causes considerably less fetal harm than tobacco and illicit drugs.

Alcohol and Children

The sedative effects of alcohol have long been treasured by nursing mothers, both on themselves and their babies. The alcohol concentration in breast milk is directly proportional to the mother's blood-alcohol level, but is much lower. A blood-alcohol concentration as high as 120mg/100ml, the result of drinking about six units of alcohol (the example given in the Royal College of Physicians' report, but surely of an unusually careless or worried mother?), would translate into a baby's blood-alcohol level of only 10mg/100ml, the same as an adult would notch up after drinking less than a glass of wine. The Physicians conclude, on the basis of some 1985 Australian research: "An occasional drink by the mother before breast feeding will not harm the baby". The new mothers of the world heave a sigh of relief.

Babies and children may well receive much more direct doses of alcohol from the medicine cabinet. As detailed in Chapter Eleven, Alcohol In Britain's Social Life, cough medicines such as Paediatric Benylin and sedatives such as Phenergan and Vallergan contain about four per cent ethyl alcohol, just as gripewater does. Taking into account the difference in body weights, these medicines probably have an effect on children similar to the same volume of brandy or gin on a fully-grown adult, although the smaller the baby or child, the more pronounced the effect.

Perhaps the most serious alcohol problem among young children is what is officially known as the "Sunday Morning Syndrome", whereby parents leave strong drink within reach of infants who guzzle it while their parents are sleeping off the effects of the night before. The adverse, sometimes extremely serious, effects of sudden high alcohol intake on a small child can be exacerbated by the fact that on Sunday mornings their stomachs are usually empty, which can cause hypoglycaemia.

Hangovers

Much as drinkers might treasure more information on hangovers, there is an understandable reluctance to divert research funds to further study of this entirely self-inflicted injury. In the Register of UK Alcohol Research 1985-1986, a bulky volume which lists more than 400 alcohol research projects, precisely one, in Liverpool, is concerned with the hangover (compared with nearly 40 in the "Services for problem drinkers, Needs and service provision" category).

There is also a lack of agreement among both the medical profession and the drinking public on what constitutes a hangover. And there is the additional complication that those who consume the most, and are therefore most likely suffer hangovers most often, are the least willing to admit to them. Although there is individual variation in susceptibility to hangovers, the habitual drinker's typical morning cry is: "I never get hangovers, but I do feel a bit rough this morning." He may well be experiencing symptoms that would keep an infrequent drinker in bed all day. If one is used to waking up with a headache, this is accepted as the norm. The joke about how awful it must be for teetotallers to wake up in the morning and know that's the best they're going to feel all day is a good indication of these tricks we play on ourselves and others.

The most common symptoms of hangover are a cocktail of depression, headache, nausea, tiredness, tremulousness, dizziness and hypersensitivity, especially to noise and light.

Many of us feel that certain drinks have a greater power than others to ambush us into a hangover. As has been explained, drinkers, and particularly women, vary in their ability to absorb alcohol. How the drinks were drunk must play a part, too. But perhaps the most important factor in causing a hangover, other than the obvious one of how much alcohol is drunk, is the form in which it is taken.

Drinks with the most congeners, the rather vague collective name for vegetable, mineral and chemical substances such as traces of metals, ethyl acetate, anthocyanins and higher alcohols absorbed either from the raw materials of the drink or the vessel in which it was made, are most likely to cause discomfort the morning after. These are highest in dark-coloured drinks matured in wood and can vary in concentration from 0.03 grams per litre of vodka, the purest drink both in terms of hangover and smell (and also usually sold at a slightly lower strength than most traditional spirits), to 2.85 grams per litre in bourbon.

Port, especially vintage port, a wine fortified with young brandy whose congeners have usually been trapped in the bottle for several decades, and brandy are notoriously congeneric, but they probably receive more than their fair share of blame for a hangover simply because they tend to be drunk last, after a considerable intake of alcohol in other forms. Congeners are metabolized in a quite different way to ethyl alcohol, and the symptoms of this metabolism are closely associated with hangover symptoms. There is very little evidence, however, to suggest that congeners themselves (which have not, in this sense, yet been embraced by the Oxford English Dictionary) are responsible for any long-term physical harm.

Despite common mythology, mixing drinks has never been scientifically established as a cause of hangover.

Dehydration is another cause of hangover. Alcohol is a diuretic, but its effects can be mitigated somewhat by taking diluted alcoholic drinks or considerable amounts of nonalcoholic drinks concurrently. Many wine drinkers try to consume at least as much water as wine at the table, and any advice on safe drinking includes the advice to make every other drink a soft one.

Like any other depressant drug, alcohol in single large doses causes over-excitability of the nervous system as the concentration of the drug in the system falls. This is why drinkers can feel particularly restless and wakeful if they wake in the middle of the night, and some of the hangover symptoms are the symptoms of withdrawal. This is the principle behind the remedy known as the hair of the dog. The hypersensitivity, for example, may be a physical compensation for the depression of the nervous system effected by the alcohol. These uncomfortable physical compensatory measures will cease if the body is given another dose of what it has become accustomed to, alcohol. This may stop the immediate hangover symptoms but can only delay the sobering up process, the return to normal for the liver, and represents an important step on the road to alcohol dependency.

Some of the individual hangover symptoms can be treated. Liquid, even the morning after, helps combat the dehydration. Caffeine, present in coffee, tea, chocolate and many colas, can help to reverse alcohol's tendency to enlarge the blood vessels in the head. Eating (anything) helps, too, with restoring blood-sugar levels, our liver having been too busy metabolizing alcohol to metabolize glucose.

There are few ways of combatting what is probably a major cause of the feeling of tiredness and depression: the perturbation of our bodies by our having narcotized ourselves and then withdrawn this depressant.

There may be a certain logic to the theory that strenuous exercise the morning after can work as a hangover cure. The alcohol is at last available to our muscles once it has been metabolized. Cold showers have their exponents, as do raw eggs, which would at least raise blood-sugar levels and provide the necessary sense of purgation, common to all of these hangover "cures". Perhaps this is further evidence of our widespread sense of guilt about drinking? Although it is surely perfectly reasonable to be extremely humble about choosing to inflict pain and despondency on oneself, some further punishment may well seem in order.

The Five-Martini Diet?

No alcoholic drink is "slimming". In fact, ethyl alcohol itself is quite high in calories, as one would expect since it is the product of fermentable sugars or carbohydrate. The calories in drinks come from two major sources, alcohol and sugar, so the most fattening drinks tend to be those that are high in both sugar and alcohol, such as port, cream sherry and liqueurs.

Of the various forms in which a unit of alcohol can be taken, straight spirits have the lowest calorific value, but that can easily be doubled if they are well diluted by a standard mixer. Standard tonics, ginger ales, colas, lemonade and fruit-based mixers are all high in calories. Only their special low-calorie versions, water and soda water are calorie-free. Drinking spirits neat keeps the calorie intake down, but this is the way to maximize alcohol's attack on the body.

Low-calorie mixers are probably not, unfortunately for slimmers, as good at mitigating the effects of alcohol as the standard prototypes.

White wine is *not* less calorific than red. Fizzy wines are no more "slimming" than still. A wine's calorific value is determined by its alcohol content and sweetness, so a Liebfraumilch, for example, which is low in alcohol but relatively high in residual sugar, may well have the same number of calories as, say, the average red or white dry wine from elsewhere that is higher in alcohol but lower in sugar. The wines with the lowest calorie count are those that are dry and low in alcohol, which generally means dry wines made farthest from the equator (with least sunshine to raise the sugar level in the grapes).

The average table wine is about or just under 12 per cent alcohol, as is champagne, but in general, the cheaper a dry wine from France, Spain or Italy, the lower it is in alcohol – although some of them, red as well as white, have a deceptively high sugar content to mitigate their high acid levels.

Sauternes, liquorous muscats and similar wines are high in both alcohol and sugar.

Among fortified wines such as port, sherry and madeira, the drier the wine the fewer the calories.

Note that Diät/Pils, despite the name, is higher in calories (and alcohol) than standard lager.

Calorific Values

Half a pint of light ale = 90 calories; of lager 80-120;
of Diät/Pils lager 90-130; of stout (e.g. Guinness) 210.
Half a pint of cider = 100-120 calories.
One unit of dry wine (1/9 bottle) = 60 calories; of low-alcohol wine 30.
One unit of dry sherry = 70 calories.
One unit of port (1/13 bottle) = 165 calories.
A single measure of gin or vodka = 55 calories; of whisky 60;
of brandy 75.
12cl of standard mixer = 40 calories; of low-calorie mixer 0 calories.

Drinking with Diabetes

A little of the right sort of alcohol is positively good for diabetics, whereas a lot could be disastrous. Drinking advice to those suffering from diabetes mellitus is very similar to that for the populace at large – if anything, even more so. Diabetes does not affect alcohol metabolism (which does not need insulin) so there is no need for diabetics to forswear alcohol, as long as they are well informed as to the carbohydrate content of different drinks.

The harmful effects of drinking on an empty stomach or of drinking neat spirits are even more pronounced in diabetics, but several medical studies suggest that moderate consumption, preferably of dry wines or diluted spirits, which are lowest in calories, can be beneficial. Some evidence suggests that moderate levels of alcohol can improve both glucose tolerance and the response of the glucose in the diabetic's blood to ingested carbohydrate. If alcohol levels get too high in insulin-dependent diabetics, however, the liver's ability to produce insulin can be fatally affected.

Several drugs commonly taken by diabetics, including tolbutamide and chlorpropamide, belong to the category of drugs whose efficacy can be severely affected by long-term heavy drinking, which can therefore jeopardize the diabetic's control of his diabetes. And up to half of all diabetics who take chlorpropamide suffer pronounced facial flushing after even a modest alcoholic intake.

CHAPTER SIX

Is Alcohol Addictive?

The Danger Signals

Semantics are not undervalued by those professionally concerned with public health and attitudes. The World Health Organization accordingly decided as long ago as 1965 that "addiction" and "addict" were words that were too emotive to be helpful. Nowadays, professionals talk about *dependence* on drugs of all sorts.

The WHO definition of dependence on any drug is: "A state, psychic and sometimes also physical, resulting from the interaction between a living organism and a drug, characterized by behavioural and other responses that always include a compulsion to take the drug on a continuous or periodic basis in order to experience its psychic effects, and sometimes to avoid the discomfort of its absence."

There can be little doubt that alcohol – like opiates such as heroin, stimulants such as cocaine and even, in some cases, caffeine, nicotine and other depressants such as Valium and sleeping pills – *can* be a drug of dependence, in certain circumstances and for certain people. Many of us have seen the most obvious examples of alcohol dependants on city streets; some of us may know others who live a much more "normal" life. But it is much less likely that an alcohol user will become dependent on alcohol than, say, an opiate user will become dependent on opiates – although the instantly addictive properties of heroin have been greatly exaggerated in European cultures. In the Far East, there are many opium smokers who are quite able to smoke the occasional pipe of opium with no more compulsion than most of us feel about an occasional glass of armagnac, for example.

In fact, of all common drug-taking activities, smoking is probably the most dependence-inducing. This last statement is carefully worded because although nicotine is the active ingredient in tobacco, experiments suggest that it is actually the habit of smoking on which many depend, intravenous injections of nicotine doing little to stave off the smoker's craving for a cigarette. Few smokers can claim they are genuinely able to take or leave their smoking habit. Alcohol appears to have much less ability to burrow down into our systems and create a compulsion. Compulsive consumption is arguably more widely associated not just with tobacco, but with the caffeine in coffee and tea, with binge eating in general, with particular foods such as chocolate, and with tranquillizers and sedatives.

This is not to say that alcohol does not have that property, to make us crave it irrationally, to make us twitchy in certain settings or at certain times of day if we are denied access to strong drink. Professionals often use the term "alcohol-dependence syndrome" to describe this phenomenon. We all react differently to alcohol's dependency potential, however, as we do in other aspects of our reaction to alcohol. Monitoring our own reactions to it and, particularly, to being denied it can help us assess how far along the road to dependency we are.

Levels of dependence on alcohol are not measured in terms of quantities drunk. Some people can be dependent on alcohol even though they may drink, only two or three times a week, quantities that others drink every day over a sustained period but can happily take or leave. The danger signals, which may well manifest themselves *after* the body has suffered a degree of physical harm, are, in roughly descending order of appearance:

The compulsion to drink at a certain time of day

Emotional upset when a drink is denied

The manipulation of routine and habits to suit, enable or favour drinking activity

Raising drinking to an activity with a higher priority than commitments to family and friends

Difficulty controlling the amount drunk

The emergence of a daily drinking routine

Altered tolerance to alcohol (the more one regularly drinks, the less intoxicated one feels – up to the point at which the liver is damaged, at which stage there is sudden drop in tolerance to alcohol)

Physical withdrawal symptoms, specifically tenseness, jitters, nausea and sweatiness, upon abstention

Drinking to avoid withdrawal symptoms.

What Is an Alcoholic?

Once it has been established that certain people can become dependent on alcohol, the most obvious next question is: "What is an alcoholic?". The usual facetious answer, which seems to have a great deal of social force, is: "Someone who drinks more than I do". The professional answer, on this semantically squeamish side of the Atlantic at least, is: "Someone who suffers from alcohol-dependency syndrome". Current medical thinking in Britain (although it is by no means embraced by all those working in the field) is that the amount each of us drinks represents a point on a continuum, along which we are all free to move forward or back.

This strikes me as an encouraging and useful way of viewing a potential problem, reflected in the early 1980s when many of Britain's Alcoholism Clinics changed their name to Alcohol Problem Centres. But in America the most popular view, fundamental to that admirably successful American-born organization Alcoholics Anonymous, for example, is that alcoholism is a disease to which certain people may be particularly susceptible physically – possibly even chemically, through their enzymatic inability to metabolize alcohol. This theory, central to American medical practice (and funding), offloads the burden of guilt from both the drink itself and from the drinker, but is unsatisfactory in that it takes the emphasis away from a number of different kinds of medical damage that alcohol can do to much more moderate drinkers.

The corollary of the disease concept of alcoholism is that the afflicted should abstain altogether – possibly, in the case of many Alcoholics Anonymous members, substituting AA activities for drinking activities. This sort of solution to problem drinking would by no means suit everyone. Indeed, it may well be the fear that they will be forced into total abstention that makes many alcohol dependants unwilling to seek help. Other forms of alcohol treatment that reintroduce the abuser to moderate consumption have also proved successful, especially with those whose problems are treated before they reach 40. Different minds and bodies undoubtedly call for different solutions to any alcohol problems they may have – although sober assessment of the efficacy of various treatments usually shows that whichever method is used, from full-scale AA indoctrination to a sympathetic chat with a well-informed nurse, a third of those treated improve, a third deteriorate and a third continue as before.

But it is the continuum theory that seems particularly useful for readers of this book. The continuum starts, of course, at total abstention and would end at a fatally high alcoholic intake. As has already been pointed out, some of us – although by no means all – might suffer medical harm as a result of our alcohol intake before our drinking reached such a point on the continuum that we became dependent on it. But the points on the continuum at which we suffer physical damage or become dependent would be different for each individual (which is why it is difficult to give precise safe limits of alcohol consumption). There undoubtedly are individuals who simply cannot handle alcohol, for reasons examined in the next section. For them, the point on the continuum at which dependency applies is tragically early. Some of the rest of us could drink as heavily or even more so without becoming dependent, but we might be damaging ourselves in other ways of which it is important to be aware.

Professionals use several standard questionnaires to determine which of their patients have alcohol problems. One of the most widely used is called MAST (Michigan Alcoholism Screening Test), of which the following is the abbreviated version. A score of five or more points is generally thought to be indicative of alcohol dependency.

QUESTIONNAIRE

Do you feel you are a normal drinker?	yes	no (2 pts)
Do friends or relatives think you are a normal drinker?	yes	no (2 pts)
Have you ever attended a meeting of Alcoholics Anonymous?	yes (5 pts)	no
Have you ever lost friends or girlfriends or boyfriends because of drinking?	yes (2 pts)	no
Have you ever got into trouble at work because of drinking?	yes (2 pts)	no
Have you ever neglected your obligations, your family, or your work for two or more days in a row because you were drinking?	yes (2 pts)	no
Have you ever had delirium tremens (DTS), severe shaking, heard voices or		

seen things that were not there after heavy drinking?	yes (5 pts)	no
Have you ever gone to anyone for help about your drinking?	yes (5 pts)	no
Have you ever been in a hospital because of your drinking?	yes (5 pts)	no
Have you ever been arrested for drunken driving or driving after drinking?	yes (2 pts)	no

The "Drinking Personality"

The society in which we live, its attitudes to drink and drunkenness, and the availability and relative cost of alcohol in our individual lives all play a part in determining how much we drink. But there are clearly other influences which interlock with these. Every population seems to yield some members who for no obvious reason embrace alcohol more enthusiastically than others. Is this because of the way they were born, the way they were brought up, or because they have a particular sort of personality?

The diversity and complexity of material on the factors that predispose some people to become dependent on alcohol is almost overwhelming, which is why there are no simple answers to this question. Specific medical damage can be inspected and recorded quite rapidly and efficiently on an individual basis, but the time span of sociological and genetic research is much more protracted, and the variables considerably more difficult to control and assess.

It is widely thought, for example, that there is some genetic input into our individual predispositions to both alcohol damage and alcohol dependency. The "twin studies" so useful to students of genetics have shown that identical twins exhibit much more similar patterns of drinking and alcohol abuse than non-identical twins.

The relatives of those with drinking problems seem to have a higher-than-average likelihood of developing alcohol problems themselves. According to one study, 25 per cent of close male relatives of alcohol abusers become abusers themselves and between five and ten per cent of close female relatives, whereas the rate of alcohol abusers among the population as a whole is five per cent for men and one per cent for women (although the female rate may well have increased since this study was published in 1982).

Genes may not entirely explain this imbalance, of course. Families almost certainly create or belong to drinking (or non-drinking) environments so that the son of a heavy drinker learns heavy drinking behaviour, just as the son of a doctor absorbs some elements of a medical environment. Others argue that there is such a thing as a "drinking personality", that some of us may simply be born more likely to drink heavily than others. Certainly some of the many reasons for drinking involve some personality change. Many drinkers treasure alcohol for its ability to awaken in them forms of behaviour they find more difficult when completely sober: flirting, talking, writing, performing are just some examples.

The hypothesis that the drinking personality exists is far from proven, however. In fact, the only major piece of research on the subject, reported by Harvard psychiatrist George Vaillant in 1983, found little evidence to support the theory. Of 500 men first assessed in great detail as young teenagers in 1940, and 200 first studied as undergraduates at Harvard in 1938, little correlation could be found in terms of personality traits in youth and behaviour towards alcohol in adult life. There was a correlation between alcohol abuse and only three of the many hundreds of factors analysed in the sample: family history of alcohol abuse, behavioural problems in adolescence and ethnic background, those with Irish, Polish and Russian backgrounds, in particular, being the most predisposed.

There are also those who are mentally ill in some way quite unrelated to alcohol but who may develop a drinking problem because of it. The mental illness most commonly associated with excessive drinking is depression, with a number of sufferers treating their own misery, perhaps caused by a specific life event, with alcohol. These sufferers treasure alcohol for its apparently euphoric short-term effects without realizing, initially, that it is itself a depressant, and that the after-effects of a drinking bout are likely to intensify the feelings of depression. Quite often members of this subgroup have behaved or are behaving compulsively in some other way, perhaps as anorexics or abusers of other drugs, either prescribed or illicit.

Some people, therefore, for a wide variety of reasons, are more likely than others to become dependent on alcohol, to reach a level of drinking that increasingly dictates their lives. Everyone, however, *could* reach that level. It is important that all social drinkers regularly monitor their own drinking behaviour, perhaps by using the alcohol-dependency test on pages 95-96, and that those who know there is some history of alcohol abuse in their own family are particularly wary.

CHAPTER SEVEN

How Much Is Enough?

The Official Limits

It is not odd that we should ask this question. Those of us who enjoy drinking naturally seek a shorthand method of limiting our consumption, rather than immersing ourselves in the arcane detail of the latest medical research data and constantly monitoring how it applies to us. It should be clear by now, however, that what *is* odd is that any official attempt has been made to answer it.

Chapter Five, What Alcohol Does to Individuals, shows that it does very different things to different people after they have drunk very different amounts of alcohol in very different ways. It also shows that, quite independently of any physical damage, drinking can result in antisocial behaviour, changed personality and even severe dependence. There is no simple equation whereby x grams of alcohol a day or week will automatically entail a certain form or amount of harm.

Physical damage *usually* predates dependence, but the early stages of physical damage, most commonly to the liver, manifest few symptoms and can be difficult to diagnose. All the more reason, therefore, to want what we know to be an unattainable ideal: "safe limits" of alcohol consumption, within which we feel assured we can drink without substantially increasing our chances of harm.

Any such limits are so difficult to define not only because there is so much individual variation in susceptibility, but because most of the available data on amounts drunk is so questionable. Those who have suffered alcohol-induced cirrhosis, gastritis or cancer of the oesophagus, for example, can hardly be expected to provide accurate records of their drinking habits over the last decades. Even those monitored prospectively rather than retrospectively, in terms of any alcohol-related damage they may suffer, may also be less than frank. Most research necessarily relies on self-reporting of drinking habits, usually over at least the past week, since so many drink in what might be called a weekly cycle dominated by the weekend. This is notoriously unreliable – not only because of the frailty of human memory (particularly the alcohol-impaired memory), but because so few of us are honest, even to ourselves, about the amount we drink.

Several surveys have shown that the amount we admit to drinking and the amount of alcoholic drink HM Customs & Excise know is put on the market is awry by almost 100 per cent.

The problem is exacerbated by the widespread ignorance of the exact alcoholic content of the varied forms in which alcohol is available. Market research shows that the average consumer is extremely hazy about the alcohol content of different drinks (it is to be hoped that the compulsory labelling of alcohol content from May 1988 will help public awareness of alcoholic intake). Alcohol is also often served in such a way as to make monitoring extremely difficult, particularly in the home. Glasses are topped up at random; mixed drinks are served in no particular proportion or quantity.

As Professor R. E. Kendell, Dean of the Faculty of Medicine of the University of Edinburgh, pointed out rather wistfully at his Institute of Psychiatry lecture in London in 1987: "Imagine how alcohol research would be transformed if we had a biochemical measure which reflected long-term blood-alcohol levels in the way that glycolysated haemoglobin reflects blood-sugar levels." This highlights just how much guesswork has to be used by the medical profession in correlating actual intake with the resulting harm that is observed. It is hardly surprising, therefore, that the notion of "safe limits" for drinking is such a controversial one among professionals treating and analysing alcohol problems. And the public must feel justifiably confused, possibly even cheated, by the edicts issued on the subject in recent years.

As recently as 1982, the Royal College of Psychiatrists was recommending as "reasonable guidelines for the upper limit of drinking" a daily intake of 60-80 grams of alcohol (roughly four pints of beer, four double measures of spirits or one standard-sized bottle of 11 per cent wine), whereas the defining paper in the *British Medical Journal*'s *ABC of Alcohol* published that year promised that 60 grams of alcohol a day for men (three pints of beer, or wine or spirit equivalents) and 30 grams for women was "safe".

Then, less than five years later, the Royal Colleges of Psychiatrists and Physicians published their provocatively named reports *Alcohol: Our Favourite Drug* and *A Great and Growing Evil* respectively. A bit of behind-the-scenes manoeuvring ensured that they broadcast the same message: that more than 400 grams of alcohol a week for men (the equivalent of 25 pints), or 280 grams a week for women, greatly increases the risk of personal harm; and that "sensible limits" of drinking, at which the risks of personal harm are low, are 168 grams of alcohol a week (an, approximate average of three units of alcohol a day – see pages 102-103 for what constitutes a "unit") for men and 112 grams a week (an average of two units a day) for women.

This new rigour in the broadcast message, effectively cutting the amounts of alcohol the common man feels he can drink with impunity by 60 per cent and the common woman's by 50 per cent, may have been so dramatic as to have been counterproductive. It is not difficult to think of sectors of male British society in which the idea of limiting alcohol consumption to one and a half pints of beer a day is so unrealistic as to be laughable. And many of those who did bother to absorb this new message from the guardians of the nation's health must have seen some contradiction between it and the medical profession's own relationship with alcohol.

This relationship may now be less passionate, according to the most recent analyses of cirrhosis mortality in doctors, reflecting a concerted effort to better educate new doctors and nurses. But the world's medical practitioners still manifest a certain *tendresse* for strong drink (remove the doctors from any wine society and the membership is crippled). Privately, many medical practitioners deprecate these new "sensible limits" as being unrealistically low (in many cases for their own drinking habits) and are suggesting their own limits, closer to old limits, at which the risks of harm increase considerably.

There is also the problem that we always suspect the medical profession of overstating its case: of being unnecessarily cautious in its demands of us, reckoning that we are bound to cheat a bit anyway. Some cynics even argue that these relatively low "sensible limits" were devised by the alcohol-treatment professionals in order to encourage more funds in their direction. Whatever the motivation, there is deep and widespread resistance to adopting this "sensible" drinking behaviour, particularly since many of us drink precisely to subjugate our more sensible impulses.

However betrayed we may feel, we should not be surprised that the officially counselled limits of alcohol consumption change as new medical evidence comes to light and the social climate evolves. In the France of the 1950s, for example, "moderate drinking" was officially anything up to a bottle of wine a day for men and half a bottle a day for women. By the 1980s these limits had been halved.

Drinking Limits in Practice

Clearly, the amount of alcohol drunk on a single occasion can result in a wide range of undesirable effects: increased aggression and its social results; a hangover; driving when drunk and even what the Americans call "vehicular homicide"; other sorts of accident; alcoholic coma; even death. But this chapter is concerned with the long-term effects of regular drinking. It should be clear by now that drinking over a long period at levels considerably below those sufficient to cause alcohol dependency does appear to increase the risk of harm, and that various groups of people are particularly vulnerable.

It might be helpful at this point to summarize the most common types of alcohol-related long-term medical harm, highlighting those people most at risk, and outlining the average amounts of alcohol that have been shown to increase that risk substantially. The various forms of harm are listed in approximately decreasing order of how commonly they occur. (See also Chapter Five, What Alcohol Does to Individuals, for more detailed information). It is important to remember, however, that although it has been proved that alcohol directly causes liver damage, the link with breast cancer, for example, is so far simply statistical.

Links for which medical explanations are not fully established, and which may be merely statistical correlations or one of several factors, some others of which may be more important than alcohol, have been marked *. One modest drink contains eight grams of alcohol.

Fatty Liver

Most at risk: women, *blacks, *those with certain antigens in their body tissue.

Substantially increased risk at more than: in men, 40 grams of alcohol a day increases risk over non-drinkers six-fold and 80 grams increases it 60-fold; in women, 20 grams of alcohol a day increases the risk three-fold, 60 grams increases it nine-fold. (The average male liver cannot metabolize more than 80 grams in any 24 hours and female livers can be less effective.)

High Blood Pressure

(and therefore strokes)

Most at risk: hypertensives.

Substantially increased risk at more than: 120 grams of alcohol a day (although those drinking 10-20 grams of alcohol a day have rather lower blood pressure, among women especially, than total abstainers). If a hypertensive is a heavy drinker the risk of a stroke is doubled, just as heavy drinkers have an increased risk of heart damage.

Gastritis

Most at risk: those with gastric or duodenal ulcers.

Substantially increased risk at: continued daily drinking.

Cirrhosis

Most at risk: women, *blacks, *those with certain antigens in their body tissue.

Substantially increased risk at more than: in men, 40 grams of alcohol daily doubles the risk and more than 80 grams daily increases the risk more than 100-fold. In women, 20 grams a day more than doubles the risk and more than 60 grams a day increases the risk 14-fold. Other studies have suggested that 80 grams of alcohol a day increases the risk of advanced cirrhosis 38-fold for men and 100-fold for women.

Cancer of the Oesophagus

Most at risk: *smokers, *spirits drinkers?

Substantially increased risk at more than: 80 grams of alcohol a day. Risk increases 18-fold if they also smoke 20 cigarettes a day.

HEAVY DRINKERS ONLY

Alcohol Dependency

Most at risk: not yet established, but some combinations of genetic and personality characteristics seem to be involved.

Substantially increased risk at more than: 96 grams of alcohol a day, although there is much individual variation.

Sexual Problems

Most at risk: alcohol abusers.

Substantially increased risk at levels necessary for alcohol dependence.

Nutritional Problems and Brain Damage

Most at risk: alcohol abusers.

Substantially increased risk at levels necessary for alcohol dependence.

Chronic Pancreatitis

Most at risk: alcohol abusers.

Substantially increased risk after: 17-18 years of heavy drinking for men; 10-11 years for women.

WOMEN ONLY

*Breast Cancer

Most at risk: obese women with a family history of breast cancer, whose first pregnancy was after 30, whose diet is high in fat.

Substantially increased risk at: 24-72 grams of alcohol a week (by 30 per cent); more than 72 grams a week, risk increases by 60 per cent.

*Miscarriage/Low Birthweight

Most at risk: women whose pregnancies are at risk for other reasons.

Substantially increased risk at: 80 grams of alcohol drunk on any single occasion during the first three months of pregnancy.

*Fetal Damage

Most at risk: alcohol abusers, who also smoke, indulge in other drugs and are poorly nourished.

Substantially increased risk at more than: 80 grams of alcohol a day.

On this basis, those who are least likely to suffer alcohol-related harm are white non-smoking men who do not have high blood pressure, ulcers or any family history of alcohol abuse and do not, according to American research, have Polish or Irish antecedents.

For most men, it is liver damage that suggests the first brake on alcohol consumption. Fatty liver may be treatable if caught in time but cirrhosis is more grave. Cirrhosis may be relatively rare (2,582 deaths in England and Wales in 1985, as compared with more than 100 times that number of deaths from diseases of the circulatory system), but it is also extremely dangerous. The risk appears to increase with the average daily amount consumed; there is no J-shaped curve here (see page 26) as in the incidence of heart disease and high blood pressure, whose curves suggest that up to 20 grams of alcohol a day is good for us. It would seem, therefore, that for most male drinkers, at least, a "sensible" upper limit on average daily consumption would fall somewhere between 20 grams and 40 grams, or between two and a half and five units of alcohol a day – and there is some evidence to suggest that drinking at the bottom end of this bracket is better than total abstention.

Women, on the other hand, have cause to worry about any consumption at all in view of the new research on breast cancer, although this link is not medically (as opposed to statistically) of very high status yet. Even if no causal link is found between alcohol and breast cancer, there is no doubt that the female liver is more susceptible to alcohol-related damage, or that the female liver recovers from such damage with much more difficulty than the average male liver. The risk of liver damage appears to increase at about 20 grams of alcohol a day and to increase substantially past 60 grams. While the breast cancer link seems a possibility, it would seem wise for women (who are not pregnant or intending to conceive, in which case they would be well advised to have only one or two drinks on only one or two occasions a week) to limit their consumption to 20 grams, or between two and three units of alcohol, a day – the equivalent of just a third of an average bottle of wine, much as it pains this writer to admit it.

The only slight compensation for those who feel that these upper limits are uncomfortably low is to consider the following. Much of the data on which the above conclusions are based has come from self-reported drinking. How much do *you* think the man with the fatty liver who said he drank three drinks a day really drank?

What Is a Drink, Anyway?

The preceding section has been carefully written referring to specific amounts of alcohol, because the only way to relate different drinks in terms of their potency and toxicity is to compare how much straight ethyl alcohol they contain. But none of us drinks grams of alcohol. We take a glass of this and a measure of that, few of us being too sure of the exact alcohol content of the this or that.

The professionals are well aware of this problem and have done their best to devise a standard, widely comprehensible measure of alcohol: the "unit". But even the "unit" has been subject to change. In 1982, in the *British Medical Journal*'s *Alcohol Problems*, a unit of alcohol was ten grams. In the more sober climate in which the Royal Colleges' reports on alcohol were published, in 1986-87, this had been pared down to eight grams, which researchers point out is *roughly* the amount of alcohol to be found in the following drinks (but see the table of alcoholic strengths below):

A half pint of beer
A standard pub measure of spirits
A glass of wine
A small glass of fortified wine such as sherry or port.

On this basis, the Royal College of Physicians could present as "sensible limits of drinking" not more than 21 units a week for men and not more than 14 units a week for women, with two or three alcohol-free days during which to rest the liver. This is admirably clear cut, but the subject deserves rather more detailed study by the intelligent, health-conscious drinker. Obviously the form in which the alcohol is drunk – whether it is still or sparkling, sweet or dry, high or low in congeners – and how it is taken will govern its effect as well as its alcohol content. But it is worth looking at exactly what eight grams of alcohol means in terms of the many drinks now available, the specific gravity of ethyl alcohol being about 0.79g per ml.

Strengths and "Units" of Alcohol

This table would look considerably simpler were it not for our imperial measurement heritage. The complexity of these calculations is sufficient to make one see the sense of total metrication, even if it entailed the abolition of the traditional pint. A standard wine glass would help, too.

Beers

There is considerable variation in strength between particular beers, and even between summer and winter brews in one or two individual brands.

1.0% (0.5–1.5%) Low-alcohol beers: a litre, or one and three-quarter pints

3.0% Mild: just over half a pint

3.7% (actually 3.2–4%) Bitter and normal lager: 0.45 of a pint, i.e. several sips less than half a pint, or rather more than half (0.59) of a standard 15oz bottle

4.0% Guinness, other stouts and premium lager: 25cl, or 0.43 of a pint, i.e. quite a bit less than half a pint

5.8% "Pils" or "Diät" lager: 17cl, or about a third of a pint

Up to 8.0% Strong ale/barley wine/special lager: 12.5cl, or a fifth of a pint

Speciality ales such as Thomas Hardy's Ale can go up to 12.5%, stronger than the average wine

Ciders

A standard bottle contains 100cl. A pint contains nearly 57cl.

3.0% Lower-alcohol cider: 33cl, or just over half a pint

4.0–4.5% Commercial ciders: 22-25cl, or between a third and just under half a pint

7.5% Dry or extra-strong cider: 13cl, or a fifth of a pint

Wines

A standard bottle contains 75cl.

18.0% Most ports, sherries, madeiras and vermouths: a thirteenth of a bottle

16.0% Amarone Italian reds, Sauternes and some muscats: a twelfth of a bottle

14.0% Some wines from California, Italy and North Africa: a tenth of a bottle

12.0% The typical better-quality wines, particularly from the southern half of Europe, and most sparkling wines, including champagne: a ninth of a bottle

11.0% Cheaper, sweeter table wines and some German dry wines: an eighth of a bottle

9.0% Cheaper, or very sweet German wines: just over a seventh of a bottle

Spirits

40.0% Gin/whisky/brandy/Pernod/full-strength liqueurs: just under a standard single 1/6 gill English pub measure, or quite a gulp less than a standard 1/5 gill Scottish pub measure

37.5% Vodka: just over a standard English pub measure of 1/6 gill

28.0% Malibu: just over one and a half standard pub single measures

23.4% Campari and Bezique: nearly a standard pub double measure

17.0% Bailey's Irish Cream and other cream liqueurs: just over a standard pub double measure

So half pints of the most popular beers actually contain rather more than eight grams of alcohol, as do single spirit measures (and who pours those outside licensed premises?). It would be salutary, and extremely sensible, if everyone who regularly drinks spirits outside licensed premises compared what they usually regard as "a Scotch", say, with the single pub measure which contains just over eight grams of alcohol.

It is also important to realize that there are geographical variations. Standard spirit measures in Scottish pubs are not 1/6 of a gill but 1/5 of a gill, which means that all of the above spirit quantities should be cut considerably in Scotland. In Ireland, they really take their drinking seriously, with the standard single measure of 1/4 of a gill known disparagingly as "a half measure". And all over the British Isles there are hotels and restaurants that serve only double measures anyway.

Note, too, how inexact is the equation "one unit of alcohol equals a glass of wine". The average nonfortified wine is about 12 per cent alcohol. The average glass of wine poured in a pub may be one seventh of a bottle, but in the home most glasses contain at least a sixth of a bottle. A sixth of a bottle of 12 per cent wine contains not eight grams of alcohol but 11.85 grams, nearly half as much again. So although the typical half pint may contain about the same amount of alcohol as the single measure of the most popular spirits, the average glass of better-quality wine contains quite a bit more. (I wonder how the Royal Colleges came to be so misled about the strength of wine?)

Even if we can govern the amount poured into our glass – either because it is a standard pub measure or, domestically, because we pour it ourself – within the categories beers, ciders, wines and spirits there is considerable variation in alcoholic strength, with the strongest in each category being well over twice as alcoholic as the weakest.

The "unit" form of measurement as publicly proclaimed ("one unit equals a half pint of beer equals a single spirit measure equals a glass of wine") is therefore not enough to give us a true picture of the alcohol we consume. Of course, the odd flirtation with a barley wine on the part of a habitual lager drinker will not immediately result in cirrhosis. But anyone who drinks regularly any beer stronger than standard lager, bitter or cider, or full-strength spirits in circumstances where standard measures are not served (such as anyone's home), or who regularly drinks wines other than Germany's low-alcohol ones, will need to know more than the standard gospel on the number of "drinks" per week he or she is allowed.

Some of the difficulties of monitoring alcohol consumption, quite apart from the variation in alcoholic strength of the drinks themselves, have already been mentioned: the social practice of topping-up half-full glasses; the variation in size of glasses; the difficulty of judging the alcoholic strength of mixed drinks (particularly home-mixed cocktails); the variation in the size of standard pub measures. (See, too, Chapter Eleven.)

But it is worth comparing how much the average drinking Briton actually drinks with these guidelines from the medical profession. Our average per capita consumption of alcohol in 1985 was 7.1 litres, which works out at 108 grams of alcohol or just over 13 "units" a week for everyone, even though official estimates put the proportion of abstainers, occasional drinkers and "light infrequent" drinkers as high as 42 per cent in 1982. This suggests that those who do drink regularly are drinking considerably more than the "sensible" weekly limits of 168 grams for men and 112 grams for women advised by the medical profession.

Indeed, Dr Marsha Morgan of the Royal Free Hospital in Hampstead, London – admittedly one of those areas of Britain one might expect to be harder-drinking than most – has analysed the drinking habits of the patients of three nearby practices and found that a good third of them are drinking at levels the medical profession regards as distincty "hazardous".

From all this we can deduce that anyone drinking more than two units a day is drinking more than the national average, an average spread over all adults, drinkers or not; and that the medical profession will have their work cut out to get us all down to the levels they consider "sensible".

CHAPTER EIGHT

How to Handle Drink

Attitudes, or What to Think

The single most important thing we can do to improve our attitude towards alcohol is simply to become aware of it and, particularly, how much of it we ingest. For too long most of us have drunk unthinkingly what we feel like drinking, when and how society expects us to, without properly considering the exact alcohol content of what we drink or how it might affect our health and behaviour in the long and short term.

But part of this proposed cognizance of one of the most potent substances we consume is that we also look drinking in the eye and embrace it for the good it can do us. This necessarily involves admitting to ourselves why we drink, acknowledging that alcohol has the power to change our perceptions, our actions and our character, that it is, in short, a psychoactive drug. Once we have accepted that, we give ourselves the opportunity to control the drug, to choose how and when we use it and, provided we inform ourselves well and are not one of the unfortunate minority who is ultra-sensitive to alcohol dependency, to what degree and extent. In other words, always actively to choose to drink rather than simply acquiesce in a general social movement towards the bottle.

Heavy drinking in the middle of a heavy working day seems particularly unwise in this light, for example. But as a counterbalance to that, I see no reason why we should not indulge with great gusto in celebratory drinking on occasion. In fact, on several medical counts it is much more harmful to drink a little and often than a lot infrequently, as long as the drinker is used to alcohol and the level of drinking is never more than, say, ten units of alcohol for men or seven for women (but see the Guide on pages 113-114). Certainly in terms of potential liver damage, the weekend blowout followed by the weekday dryout, during which the liver can rest from the onslaught, is the ideal model, provided the weekend blowout is not too literal.

In a social sense, perhaps the most useful change of attitude needed is a reversal of society's general urge to push as much alcohol as possible down other people's throats, whatever the situation. If we could rid ourselves of our inherited view that the prime symbol of social generosity is the provision and repeated application of strong drink, we might save ourselves considerable harm and expense, not to mention social discomfort. The person who simply doesn't want to drink, or shouldn't drink for medical reasons, would never feel a wet blanket for refusing to join more bibulous companions. Hosts would not press on guests the "chaser", the "nightcap", the "other half" and, particularly "one for the road", and would provide nonalcoholic alternatives as a matter of course. Drinking should be a question of personal responsibility, not social duty.

Admiration for those who drink heavily with no apparent ill-effects is misplaced. Little skill is required in those we call, perhaps significantly, often admiringly, "hard" drinkers.

Choosing, or What (and How) to Drink

It will be clear from Chapters Six and Seven that different drinks vary enormously in their alcoholic content and potency. The first step to responsible drinking is to get a grasp on the alcohol levels of whatever we drink with any frequency, and to pinpoint those drinks that are most alcoholic so that we are particularly wary of them. At long last there is legislation that requires the drinks industry to tell us how much alcohol each drink contains on the same, percentage-by-volume, scale. (This affects drinks packaged from May 1988, but some drinks labelled before then are expected to remain in the distribution system for some time.)

Of spirits, the most powerful are some malt whiskies that are not "broken down" or diluted to the usual strength of 40 per cent but are sold at up to 60 per cent (notably by the connoisseurs' buying group, the Scotch Malt Whisky Society of Edinburgh); a few similar special bottlings of various brandies and rums; "Polish Pure Spirit" at 57 per cent; Polish Wyborowa vodka Blue Label which is usually 45 per cent; the obscure Majorcan spirit cana which is 75 per cent; some Alsace Eaux-de-Vie at 42 per cent; Underberg, the supposed hangover cure, at 44 per cent; green Chartreuse, 55 per cent and the essence of it, Elixir Vegetal, 71 per cent; some Greek ouzos, schnapps and South American piscos which can be more than 40 per cent. These can be several times as strong as drinks such as cream liqueurs.

Of wines, apart from fortified wines such as port, madeira, sherry and malaga, which are usually about 18 per cent alcohol, the strongest are those made from grapes ripened in hot climates such as those from California and parts of Italy, especially where a grape-drying technique is used as in Recioto wines such as Amarone. These can be twice as strong as German wines.

The most potent beers – barley wines and daredevil lagers such as Carlsberg Special – can be nearly twice as strong as bitter or standard lager, just as ciders sold in significantly small bottles, such as Bulmer's No.7, can be twice as strong as standard medium cider.

The drinks with the most congeners – those substances thought to contribute towards hangovers and, in some individuals, particularly adverse reactions – are those that are dark coloured, aged in wood or bottled with a high proportion of dry extract, as in vintage port.

One unit (eight grams) of alcohol is to be found in:
    Half a pint of standard bitter or lager
    Just over a third (or just under a half) pint of standard cider
    A ninth of a bottle of wine at 12% alcohol
    A thirteenth of a bottle of fortified wine (sherry, port, etc.) at 18%
    Just under a standard English pub *single* measure of a sixth of a gill
    of full-strength 40% spirits such as gin or whisky

According to the medical profession, *sensible* limits of drinking are:
    For men, not more than 21 units a week, including two or three
    days without any alcohol
    For women, not more than 14 units a week, including two or three
    days without any alcohol

Study of the research data available suggests that the risk of serious alcohol-related harm increases substantially at these *hazardous* levels:
    For men, 50 units per week
    For women, 35 units per week.

So women who have been drinking half a bottle of wine a day (such as myself) are getting dangerously close to a high-risk level of drinking, while men who drink half a bottle of wine a day, plus either a pint and a half of beer a day, or any measure of spirits that is more than a standard pub double, are also approaching that limit.

Continuing at this (socially by no means abnormal) level of drinking does not necessarily entail liver damage, but the risk of it does seem to increase dramatically. It is also worth remembering the following:

The faster alcohol is absorbed, the higher is the peak blood-alcohol concentration

The slower alcohol is absorbed, the lower the peak blood-alcohol concentration but the longer it stays in the system

Eating, particularly fatty foods and carbohydrates, before or while drinking delays alcohol absorption

Mixing different sorts of drinks has no proven ill-effect on the body

Sugar in drinks delays alcohol absorption

Fizzy drinks accelerate alcohol absorption

The more slowly a drink is drunk, the lower the peak alcohol concentration

Alcohol is absorbed most rapidly from drinks with an alcohol content between 15 and 30%

The liver can metabolize about one unit of alcohol per hour, rather less in women, and probably no more than eight units in 24 hours because of the "top-up" effect.

This suggests that someone who wants, to borrow drugspeak, a "quick hit" from alcohol should drink fast on an empty stomach, ideally something dry and fizzy, whereas those who want a "gentle high" would be well advised to sip slowly while eating, ideally a drink chock full of sugar (the sugar sounds far from ideal on many other grounds, however).

This theory could be put to practical use. Of couples or groups who have to drive back from a pub or party, for example, the driver who does not want to abstain completely (although this is the wisest course, since any dose of alcohol slows reactions and impairs judgement) can have one unit of alcohol, on an empty stomach for maximum effect, at the start of the evening, and no more than one every hour subsequently, stopping alcoholic intake at least an hour before the drive home. The non-drivers who can sleep off the effects throughout the night should be fine provided they space throughout

These tables show the *likely* effect of a particular rate of drinking on the amount of alcohol in the blood, according to sex and weight. Remember that 1 unit equals: 1 half pint of beer, or 1 glass of table wine, or 1 single measure of spirits. But this is very approximate. See also

MEN

BAC 50 (BREATH ALCOHOL: APPROX 23). YOU WILL FEEL QUITE PLEASANT WITHOUT BEING DRUNK. HOWEVER YOUR JUDGEMENT MAY SUFFER AND YOUR CHANCE OF ACCIDENTS WILL BE INCREASED.

	ONE HOUR	TWO HOURS	THREE HOURS	FOUR HOURS	FIVE HOURS
9 TO 11 STONES	2 UNITS	3 UNITS	4 UNITS	4½ UNITS	5 UNITS
11 TO 13 STONES	2½ UNITS	4 UNITS	5 UNITS	5½ UNITS	6 UNITS
13 ST. OR OVER	3 UNITS	4½ UNITS	5½ UNITS	5½ UNITS	6 UNITS

BAC 80 (BREATH ALCOHOL: APPROX 35). YOU WILL LOSE A LITTLE SELF-CONTROL AND YOUR REACTIONS MAY BE A LITTLE SLOWER. ALTHOUGH THIS IS THE LEGAL LIMIT FOR DRIVING, IT IS NO GUARANTEE THAT YOU'LL BE FIT TO DRIVE.

	ONE HOUR	TWO HOURS	THREE HOURS	FOUR HOURS	FIVE HOURS
9 TO 11 STONES	3½ UNITS	4 UNITS	5 UNITS	5½ UNITS	6½ UNITS
11 TO 13 STONES	4 UNITS	5 UNITS	6 UNITS	6½ UNITS	7½ UNITS
13 ST. OR OVER	5 UNITS	6 UNITS	7 UNITS	7½ UNITS	8 UNITS

BAC 120 (BREATH ALCOHOL: APPROX 55). YOU WILL GET QUITE MERRY AND YOU MAY BECOME RATHER CLUMSY AND ACT ON IMPULSE. THIS IS PROBABLY AS DRUNK AS ANYONE SHOULD GET EVEN WHEN CELEBRATING.

	ONE HOUR	TWO HOURS	THREE HOURS	FOUR HOURS	FIVE HOURS
9 TO 11 STONES	5½ UNITS	6 UNITS	6½ UNITS	7 UNITS	7½ UNITS
11 TO 13 STONES	6 UNITS	7 UNITS	8 UNITS	8½ UNITS	9 UNITS
13 ST. OR OVER	7½ UNITS	8½ UNITS	9 UNITS	9½ UNITS	10 UNITS

BAC = BLOOD ALCOHOL CONCENTRATION
BREATH ALCOHOL = THE READING ON A BREATHALYZER

the evening their intake of drinks whose alcohol content should be metabolized during the night. On the same basis, the business lunch need not be alcohol-free. An apéritif may go straight to the head, but if it is not topped up with wine during the meal, the body will be alcohol-free about an hour after it was finished (which is perhaps why the serious business of a business lunch is traditionally conducted at the end by the cunning, who only pretend to drink during the meal?). These facts also suggest that those who want to the table of alcoholic strengths of various beers, ciders, wines and spirits in Chapter Seven, *What Is a Drink, Anyway*. Most important, remember that drink affects different people in different ways, and these tables are intended to be used only as a rough guide.

WOMEN

BAC 50 (BREATH ALCOHOL: APPROX 23). YOU WILL FEEL QUITE PLEASANT WITHOUT BEING DRUNK. HOWEVER YOUR JUDGEMENT MAY SUFFER AND YOUR CHANCE OF ACCIDENTS WILL BE INCREASED.

	ONE HOUR	TWO HOURS	THREE HOURS	FOUR HOURS	FIVE HOURS
9 ST. OR UNDER	1½ UNITS	2 UNITS	2½ UNITS	3 UNITS	3½ UNITS
9 TO 11 STONES	2 UNITS	2½ UNITS	3½ UNITS	4 UNITS	4½ UNITS
11 ST. OR OVER	2½ UNITS	3 UNITS	4 UNITS	5 UNITS	5½ UNITS

BAC 80 (BREATH ALCOHOL: APPROX 35). YOU WILL LOSE A LITTLE SELF-CONTROL AND YOUR REACTIONS MAY BE A LITTLE SLOWER. ALTHOUGH THIS IS THE LEGAL LIMIT FOR DRIVING, IT IS NO GUARANTEE THAT YOU'LL BE FIT TO DRIVE.

	ONE HOUR	TWO HOURS	THREE HOURS	FOUR HOURS	FIVE HOURS
9 ST. OR UNDER	2½ UNITS	3 UNITS	3½ UNITS	3½ UNITS	4 UNITS
9 TO 11 STONES	3 UNITS	3½ UNITS	4½ UNITS	4½ UNITS	5½ UNITS
11 ST. OR OVER	3½ UNITS	4½ UNITS	5½ UNITS	5½ UNITS	6 UNITS

BAC 120 (BREATH ALCOHOL: APPROX 55). YOU WILL GET QUITE MERRY AND YOU MAY BECOME RATHER CLUMSY AND ACT ON IMPULSE. THIS IS PROBABLY AS DRUNK AS ANYONE SHOULD GET EVEN WHEN CELEBRATING.

	ONE HOUR	TWO HOURS	THREE HOURS	FOUR HOURS	FIVE HOURS
9 ST. OR UNDER	3½ UNITS	4 UNITS	4½ UNITS	4½ UNITS	5 UNITS
9 TO 11 STONES	4½ UNITS	5 UNITS	5½ UNITS	5½ UNITS	6 UNITS
11 ST. OR OVER	5 UNITS	6 UNITS	6½ UNITS	6½ UNITS	7 UNITS

From *So you want to cut down your drinking?* by Ian Robertson and Nick Heather for the Scottish Health Education Group, Edinburgh.

moderate alcohol's effects on the system should be particularly wary of drinks between 15 and 30 per cent alcohol, such as sherry, port, madeira, cream liqueurs and other low-strength spirits, and full-strength spirits that have been diluted with only about as much mixer again. Alcohol diluted with low-calorie mixers, without the carbohydrates which distract the system from metabolizing alcohol, is presumably absorbed faster than alcohol diluted with standard mixers which contain sugar.

Those Who Should Be Particularly Careful

The following should be particularly wary about their intake of alcohol, for a variety of reasons:

At Risk	Why
Women (and this is a sad fact, not a male conspiracy, sisters)	Liver damage, accelerated absorption of alcohol at ovulation and just before a period, possibly increased risk of breast cancer.
Pregnant women	Miscarriage, low birthweight of baby, birth defects.
Women who are trying to conceive	As above (most damage is done in the first three months, when the woman may not know she is pregnant), possibly decreased fertility.
Men whose partners are trying to conceive	Reduced sperm count.
Those with high blood pressure	Increased blood pressure, hypertension, possibly stroke.
Those with gastric or duodenal ulcer	Gastritis.
Those who have had a partial gastrectomy	Much-accelerated absorption.
Those on medication	See below.
Insulin-dependent diabetics	Excessive drinking may fatally inhibit the liver's glucose production.
Those suffering from cardiomyopathy	Heart muscle will become even more fatty if heavy drinking continues.

Drink and Other Drugs

Since alcohol is a drug, it is not surprising that it interacts with many other drugs, both illicit and prescribed. The following are the abbreviated conclusions of the Royal College of Physicians in their 1987 report on alcohol, *A Great and Growing Evil*.

Alcohol is itself a depressant and, when taken in any quantity on a single occasion, can depress the rate at which the body metabolizes other drugs and exaggerate their effects. Alcohol + depressants = disaster. Drink and Valium or Librium is not a sensible cocktail, but this is true of any drugs that act on the central nervous system, such as dextropropoxyphene which, when taken with alcohol, can be fatal. If an overdose of sleeping tablets or tranquillizers is washed down with alcohol, the resulting coma will be even more dangerous than washing down the pills with H_2O.

There is also a reciprocal effect whereby drugs acting on the central nervous system depress alcohol metabolism so that the effects of alcohol are exaggerated. The Physicians recommend a ban on alcohol with any central nervous system drugs, such as oxazepam (Oxanid), lorazepam (Ativan) and diazepam (Valium).

A single heavy drinking session results in the following drugs having an exaggerated effect: benzodiazepines, barbiturates, phenothiazines, tricyclic antidepressants (Tofranil, Prothiaden), chlormethiazole, dextropropoxyphene, monoamine oxidase inhibitors, oral hypoglycaemic agents, the anti-convulsant phenytoin, warfarin (which can cause internal bleeding when taken with alcohol) and metronidazole.

Long-term heavy drinkers are much more likely to abuse other drugs than the rest of the population. The effect of sustained use of (any one of) alcohol, cigarettes and cannabis is to increase the effectiveness of the drug metabolism rate, which can mean that therapeutic drugs are removed from the system much faster than in normal bodies. This means that normal dosages of drugs such as barbiturates, benzodiazepines, most anti-convulsants, warfarin (see above) and even paracetamol often need to be doubled for chronic alcohol abusers, and the drugs may even be dangerously ineffectual in very heavy drinkers.

There are drugs that seriously affect the metabolism of alcohol. Most famously, Antabuse is a medication specifically designed to discourage alcohol abusers from drinking by reacting badly with alcohol. It interferes with the body's mechanism for breaking down alcohol, competing with it for enzymes, and results in an excess of the toxic by-product acetaldehyde, resulting in very unpleasant reactions including severe headaches, nausea, palpitations and vomiting. Disulfiram (Antabuse), chlorpropamide, calcium carbimide, metronidazole, griseofulvin, procarbazine, sulphonylureas, chloramphenicol, furazolidone, mepacrine and chloral hydrate all produce this reaction.

There are even implications in the workplace. Thiurams used by those who make fungicides and synthetic rubber can cause a reaction with alcohol similar to that caused by Antabuse, and those who work with trichloro-ethylene find that it takes only a small amount of alcohol to make them intoxicated, and oddly blotchy.

The list of drugs and their reactions with alcohol mentioned above is by no means exhaustive. It is always sensible to check with your doctor or pharmacist when being prescribed drugs of any kind.

As for interactions between alcohol and illicit drugs, the information is, not surprisingly, sketchy, but it seems intuitively contrary to drink the depressant alcohol at the same time as any expensive stimulant.

Drinking and Driving

In no aspect of alcohol use is there a need for a greater reform of our attitude than in our recognition of the problem of drinking and driving. Many enthusiastic drinkers may well feel that they would rather risk their livers, blood pressure and gut for the rewards that alcohol can give them. That, so long as they do not neglect their families or their work because of their drinking, seems entirely their own affair.

But no one who has ever taken to the wheel of a car with some alcohol inside him or her can opt out of the drunk-driving problem, because this combination of two such potentially dangerous instruments can fatally trans-form innocent bystanders into victims.

Every year in Britain alone, between 1,000 and 2,000 people are killed in alcohol-related road accidents. The increase in drunk-driving convictions has risen far above the increase in car ownership and miles driven, increasing by nearly 40 per cent in the first four years of this decade to well over 100,000 convictions a year. Yet, almost incredibly, such a crime has had about the same social status as a parking offence. Most motorists feel united in the common cause of trying to outwit the parking warden/breath test. Those who fail do not offend; they are considered simply unlucky and, as in a child's game of tag, "get caught". Those who wriggle their way out of a conviction on a legal technicality have been hailed as ingenious heroes. Losing a driving licence is inconvenient but carries surprisingly little stigma in view of the irresponsibility of the act.

This may be partly because drinking and driving is (at the moment) such a common activity. We all do it, and have done for two or three genera-tions. And while the majority of drivers remain unaware of the exact alcohol content of each drink, it is almost impossible for them to monitor their consumption and keep blood-alcohol concentrations within legal limits.

There is also alcohol's deceptive effect on our impressions of our own behaviour. Many of us are convinced we drive better with a glass of alcohol inside us, but we must regretfully face the facts. Alcohol distorts our perceptions, enhancing particularly those that concern our own performance, whether it is in telling jokes, playing the piano or driving a car. Carefully controlled experiments have shown that even quite normal social doses of alcohol encourage us to take dangerous risks, even to attempt the impossible.

We all do it, and the longer we get away with it without hurting ourselves or anyone else (or being found out by the law), the less serious the risk seems to be.

Alcohol also slows our reactions, so that if we come across an obstacle in the road we not only need more time to see and identify it, but more time to react. There is a direct linear relationship between alcohol consumption and deterioration of driving skills which we cannot ignore.

One unit of alcohol raises the blood-alcohol level by about 15mg of alcohol per 100ml of blood in men and by about 20mg/100ml in women. The body can process about 15mg/100ml in an hour, but most of us drink more than one unit an hour in many drinking situations so there is a considerable "top-up effect". To remain under the 80mg/100ml legal blood-alcohol limit, women should be wary of drinking more than four units (five for men) unless they are carefully spaced over several hours. (See also the Self-Help Guide to Sensible Drinking on pages 113-114.)

Wider availability of accurate but unofficial breathalysers seems eminently desirable, both for the sake of drivers who may thereby escape potential accidents or convictions, and for others on the road. The breath-alcohol reading gives a direct indication of blood-alcohol concentration (BAC) according to the equivalents shown on pages 113 and 114. When timing the use of a breathalyser, it is worth remembering that although the reading may be under the limit just after drinking four or five units, BAC may well be over the legal maximum half an hour later. It is currently, sadly, the case that these unofficial breathalysers are not as accurate as those used by the police. Women and young people should also remember that it usually takes much less to get their blood-alcohol concentrations up to the legal limit than men's.

It is also sensible for those who drive abroad to inform themselves of the legal limits in other countries. Generally speaking, these are dictated less by a country's opprobrium towards drunken driving as an offence and more by the prevailing level of drinking and/or personal inconvenience caused by losing a licence. There can be few other explanations for the indulgent state of affairs in Eire, Italy, Portugal and the United States. The legal blood-alcohol limits for driving in various countries are:

Europe

Bulgaria	omg/100ml
Poland	20mg/100ml
Finland, Greece, Iceland, Netherlands, Norway, Sweden and Yugoslavia	50mg/100ml
All other countries, including the UK	80mg/100ml
Eire	120mg/100ml
Italy, Portugal	no limit

Outside Europe

India	omg/100ml
Japan, Chile	50mg/100ml
Australia (varies according to state)	50-80mg/100ml
New Zealand, Canada	80mg/100ml
USA (varies according to state)	100-150mg/100ml

We could learn more from some other countries on how to cope with both drinking and transporting ourselves. In most Scandinavian countries, for example, a driver is designated at the beginning of a drinking session and the role has a certain and defined status, not simply that of a party pooper or drudge.

Far too often in this country, it seems, the decision about who is driving is taken after drinking rather than before.

The Next Generation

Quite apart from keeping strong drinks out of reach of toddlers, it does seem that we have other alcohol-related responsibilities towards the next generation. The most important of these is to encourage young people, by example, to treat alcohol with respect.

Of the many aspects of education that seem most appropriately taught by parents rather than schools, alcohol education is surely a prime candidate. Evidence, particularly comparison of Jewish and Irish communities, suggests that considerably fewer alcohol problems will result in later life if children are introduced to alcohol sensibly by their parents in the home, rather than learning to drink in settings such as the pub in which there are fewer family restraints.

The next generation could presumably benefit greatly from seeing adults using alcohol intelligently, with respect for and detailed knowledge of its potency. The signs are that among the worryingly numerous teenage drinkers, girls are drinking far more than their mothers ever did. It seems vital to spread the message not only of the different alcohol contents of various drinks, but of the frailty of the female body as an alcohol receptor before too much harm is done.

Particularly sensitive education is needed on combining drinking with driving. Too often, fatalities result from young people combining these two activities, in both of which they are inexperienced. There are some very convincing arguments for allowing lower legal maximum blood-alcohol levels for young people than for adults.

CHAPTER NINE

Drink Throughout the Ages

The Original High

The history of drinking is remarkably central to the history of civilization. In fact the drinking of wine, almost certainly the form in which alcohol was first known, is regarded by many as an integral part of the process of civilization. Even now, wine is widely seen as the "civilized" drink, beer being for barbarians and spirits for soaks and spivs.

Wherever a civilization went, it took the production techniques (and, for an invading force, usefully stupefying effects) of its drink with it. Thus did the Romans introduce the vine to England, the Celts the art of distillation to Scotland, the European colonists the full range of alcoholic drinks to the Americas, Africa and Australasia.

Any world history that is only a chapter long is, of course, deeply suspect. This sketchy outline is no exception and could easily drive a self-respecting historian to drink. It is a genuine attempt, however, to show how attitudes to drink in different forms, and to drinking and drunkenness in general, continually evolve, or at least change.

There is no doubt that a critical point in public concern about alcohol consumption has been reached, with the World Health Organization having identified its ill-effects as "one of the world's major public health problems". It is clear, however, that this concern is not new – and that in Britain drinking is by no means at a record high. In the mid-eighteenth and late nineteenth centuries, we were drinking far more than today, and each of these peaks was followed by a peak in concern about, and attempts to curb, excessive drinking. Indeed, there is a popular theory that alcohol consumption follows prosperity and that the country's drinking patterns follow its economic cycles, which last approximately two generations. This allows a new generation to grow up in prosperous times having had no experience of the perils of drink and therefore drinking to excess – making temperance crusaders of the next generation and so on.

What makes our current position vis-à-vis drinking so potentially exciting is that we have so much excellent medical and sociological evidence to go on, and the experience of more than a century of collective action on alcohol abuse. Let us hope we are now mature enough to take personal responsibility for our drinking.

The Drug of the Ancients

Of all the mental escape routes available to man, alcohol almost certainly has the considerable distinction of being the most widespread, with ferments of astonishing ingenuity a part of local tradition all over the world. It is also almost certainly the oldest drug known to man. Edward Hyams in his *Dionysus* constructs a most persuasive case for conscious wine drinking as early as 6000 years BC in the wine vine's native land, Transcaucasia. The sheltered, fertile valley south of the Caucasus between the Black Sea and the Caspian Sea is now regarded as the greenhouse of the USSR. The Soviet authority who has most vigorously addressed the question of the antiquity of wine drinking reckons that Stone Age man was deliberately cultivating vines as early as 8000BC.

What is certain is that long before anyone started to "tame" and cultivate vines, it was discovered that something odd happened when the fruit of the vines that grew wild in Transcaucasia was collected and left for a while. The grapes would have been crushed by their own weight, the yeasts on the skin would have set to work on the sugar in the juice, and within a day or so the Adam and Eve of wines were made – although some sort of earthenware container would have to have been developed to stop the juice from simply trickling away.

One wonders how on earth those primitive men and women (because it would certainly have been the women who collected and stored the fruit) reacted to their first strong drink. A modern wine drinker would probably find the liquid pretty crude and vinegary, but it would have contained a hitherto unknown substance: ethyl alcohol. Our Neolithic forebear was presumably accustomed to unexplained experiences, but probably not to something odd that seemed to happen right inside his head. As Edward Hyams puts it, "It would have been supposed that some divine afflatus had entered him. And, as every wine lover knows, this supposition would have been correct." The "primal inebriate" would certainly have been likely to make a connection between wine and another, unearthly world.

Just to the south of this area, of course (and now just in Turkey), is Mount Ararat, where the Old Testament tells us Noah retreated from the floods with his ark and vine cuttings.

The first firm evidence we have for domestic cultivation of the vine is that the vine leaf was a standard symbol in the pictograms of much more civilized Mesopotamia, in the valleys of the Tigris and Euphrates to the south of Transcaucasia and Mount Ararat in what is now Iraq. Archeological evidence and detective work suggest that viticulture must have been well established here by 4000BC and in Egypt by 3000BC. A stroll around the British Museum can demonstrate the extent to which wine was an integral part of life in the ancient Mesopotamian city of Ur and in Ancient Egypt.

From the same part of the world that is today Iraq, a country where alcohol in any form is hardly tolerated, the useful Babylonian Code of Hammurabi, dating from about 1750BC, shows that by that time beer drinking was as common as wine drinking. Or rather, more common, in that beer was the drink of the ordinary tavern (often kept by a woman), whereas wine was more usually associated with temples and ritual – a pattern that was mirrored in Ancient Egypt and was to be repeated thousands of years later throughout northern Europe. Predating Weights and Measures Officers by more than three and a half millennia, Hammurabi spelt out punishments for those who sold beer in short measure.

Once it was discovered that the starch in grains could be converted to fermentable sugars by chewing it, by letting it get mouldy (which is how rice wine was discovered in the East), or by an ancient precursor of the malting process, beer would probably have been easier and cheaper than wine to produce in quantity in the fierce climate of Egypt and Babylonia. Although the fact that taverns were called "wine shops," and beer – even then – was called "barley wine", supports the theory that wine predated beer.

It is presumably because wine and not beer was the first mind-altering substance embraced by man that wine has been so inextricably linked with religion for so many centuries. Almost as soon as we have records of wine being drunk, we have records of its sacramental use.

This is not the place for detailed analysis of wine's role in the religious ceremonies of successive civilizations. It is remarkable, though, that wine's sacerdotal role in Hebrew religion and then in Christianity, for instance, is merely a relatively recent example of man's persistent inclination to drink and make libations as part of a religious experience. Of all the many gifts which could be and were offered up to the gods in ancient Mediterranean cultures, wine was the most popular – presumably because of its antiquity, and because its psychoactive ingredient associated it with the supernatural and religion.

The Babylonian Talmud is dotted with references to wine, and it is a comfort to many twentieth-century drinkers that wine is mentioned 150 times in the Old Testament – if a disappointment that it rates only ten mentions in the New Testament. But not all of these mentions fully condone wine drinking. Alcohol abuse has been known almost as long as alcohol. And as vine growing, and extremely sophisticated winemaking, spread over the centuries to the more temperate vineyard land of ancient Greece and thence to ancient Rome, so did reactions to overindulgence.

Noah's reproof from Jehovah for drunkenness illustrates the mores of Biblical times. The prophet Isaiah painted a picture of holy men that seems appropriate to the (distinctly secular) Benidorm barbecues of today's package-tour operators: "Priest and prophet are addicted to strong drink and bemused with wine; clamouring in their cups, confirmed topers, hiccuping in drunken stupor; every table is covered with vomit." The Book of Proverbs gave the other side of the picture: "Give strong drink unto him that is ready to perish, and wine unto them that be of heavy heart. Let him drink, and forget his poverty, and remember his misery no more."

Dionysus, originally the god of ecstasy and vegetation and eventually god of the liquid that offered a conjunction of the two, was as important in Greek mythology as was the Roman counterpart Bacchus. But drinking in ancient Greece was very much more than part of religious ritual. By Homeric times, around 700BC, wine, like corn and oil, was established as a staple of Mediterranean life – as it has remained ever since, although safe water supplies and the infiltration of cunningly marketed soft drinks has begun to erode wine's pre-eminence. Greek wine was strong and sweet and was usually drunk in diluted form, although, as Harold McGee points out in *On Food and Cooking*, the Greek word for "to breakfast", *akratidzomai*, means literally "to drink undiluted wine".

Although the Etruscans may have done much to encourage wine production in what is now Tuscany, around 200BC the wine vine really took hold in the less extreme climate and healthier vineyard environment (no locusts) of the southern half of what is now Italy – so much so that the Greeks called it Enotria, or "land of wine".

In the first century AD, Pliny wrote what was in effect the first known detailed and comprehensive wine manual, the fourteenth volume of his *Natural History*, although this was just one example of the extensive records of the Roman way with wine that are still available for study today. Pliny had reservations about wine, calling it "a thing that perverts men's minds and produces madness" and complaining: "There is no department of man's life on which more labour is spent – as if nature had not given us the most healthy of beverages to drink, water."

But with the Romans came the beginnings of connoisseurship, with records of the characteristics of many different wines being made as early as AD200. And, just as in modern times, those who wrote about wines also gave advice about hangovers (drinking cabbage water was recommended by Athenaeus). Wine, or rather its soporific effects on those not used to it, was a powerful weapon in the expansion of the Roman Empire, especially as the Romans pushed northwards into Gaul and kindled the flames of one of the most passionate of the world's love affairs, between wine and the French.

After a break in the second and third centuries AD when the Roman emperor Domitian tried to uproot vines in many areas, notably Gaul (largely to protect Enotria), the most important spread of what might be called wine-based culture took place between 500BC and AD400. By the end of the fourth century AD the wine vine, thanks largely to the Romans' enthusiasm for it, had been introduced to just about every European region in which it now flourishes, excluding Alsace for some reason but including Germany, Britain and quite a bit of northern France that is today considered too cool for commercially successful viticulture.

To the Greeks, and certainly the Romans, beer was thought to be a very poor substitute – suitable only for those who could not afford wine, or those primitive cultures in North Africa and Spain which had not mastered the arts of viticulture and vinification. Pliny remarked, "The nations of the west also have their own intoxicant, made from grain soaked with water."

Brewing expertise was certainly well understood by the ancient Egyptians, and seems to have worked its way westwards around the central and eastern Mediterranean basin that had been so effectively colonized by the vine to reach its eventual centre of operations, those parts of northern Europe where it is too cold for the vine to ripen easily.

As the Roman Empire declined, it was left to the Christian church to uphold the tradition of alcoholic drinks – chiefly winemaking – in the Dark Ages. St Martin of Tours, the first known monk/vine grower and patron saint of innkeepers, lived in the fourth century, yet even today in and around Tours on the Loire, drunkenness is called "St Martin's sickness", illustrating the robust attitude of the Catholic church – and the French – towards intoxication.

In the fifth century, the Benedictine code laid down some revealing laws of monastic behaviour towards wine. "We consider that half a pint of wine a day is sufficient for everyone. None the less, those to whom God has given the gift of abstaining should know that they will be rewarded. But in a case where the locality or the work or the heat of summer may make a larger allowance necessary, the abbot must decide, taking care that there is no excess or drunkenness. Indeed we read that wine is not a drink for monks, but since monks cannot nowadays be persuaded of this, let us at least agree to drink sparingly and not to take our fill, as 'wine maketh even the wise to fall away'."

The monks laid the foundations for many of today's wine trade routes. When, in 610, St Colombus exported wine from Nantes to his Irish brethren, he was paving the way for the oceans of Muscadet that have been used to wash oysters down Irish throats considered too sophisticated for Guinness.

Perhaps more than any other region, Burgundy can still present the evidence of its strong monastic tradition. The Abbey of Bèze was founded around 600 and governed the winemaking in such villages as Gevrey, Vosne and Marsannay. Less than 200 years later, Charlemagne gave vineyards, including those that now produce one of the world's great white wines, still called Corton-Charlemagne, to the Abbey of Saulieu. Much of the land we know today as the source of the great wines of Burgundy had been acknowledged, and was in the hands of monastic centres such as the Abbeys of Saulieu and Cluny and the Clos de Vougeot, by 1100.

The Anglo-Saxons meanwhile had been sufficiently keen on wine to import it to supplement the produce of their monastic vineyards. As the inimitable culinary historian C. Anne Wilson reports in her *Food and Drink in Britain*, by the year 982 enough was arriving from Rouen to make it worth Aethelred's while to charge a toll on it at London Bridge – perhaps the earliest example of customs duty on alcoholic beverages entering the country.

The Norman conquest in 1066, of course, did much to encourage the export of wines to England from western France, especially Rouen and Bordeaux, by the twelfth century. Beer at this time would have been the staple drink of the common man, but wine was available in quantity for religious celebration, in the monasteries, and in nobler households – so much so that Henry II, the king who so wisely married into the western half of France, was able to fine one Norman lord, Matthew de Vernum, 100 casks of wine for breach of the peace.

Alcohol as Sacrament

Make no mistake about it, civilized "western" man has always had a supply of drink to hand. Even a high proportion of the people of Central and South America, who had access to other drugs such as coca and mescaline, developed indigenous ferments of local grains or roots to supplement it. Nomadic tribesmen in Central Europe devised their own escape route from reality by fermenting the milk of their herds, while in the Far East grains, and rice in particular, have been the most popular raw materials for fermentation.

In the Middle East, the cradle of cannabis, the close relationship between drink and religion was most powerfully demonstrated in the seventh century when Mahomet outlawed wine, the only form of alcohol then known, to all followers of his Islamic faith. The irony is that the effect of this stricture has been to wipe out viniculture from the potentially important area in which it first flourished. It is true, however, that alcohol consumption in the ancient Persian Empire had been thought worthy of note even by visiting Greeks. Herodotus noted that even the weightiest matters of the day would be formally debated twice, once drunk and once sober. Xenophon was horrified that the average Persian left a banquet horizontally rather than vertically. From this background came the Koran and subsequently a huge and expanding culture which continues to eschew alcohol, officially at least, although Omar Khayyam was by no means the last Muslim to appreciate the unique appeal of fine wine.

There was further irony in the Islam stance on strong drink. It was the Moors who were responsible for disseminating the technique of distillation, separating out wine's intoxicating essence, and for the derivation of its name, alcohol. The Arab alchemists developed their distillates in the twelfth and thirteenth centuries, although the Chinese may well have made the technical breakthrough many centuries earlier. Certainly the ancient Egyptians, and even Aristotle, had alembics which could have yielded alcohol had they thought of putting wine through them. It took several centuries, however, for distilled spirits to evolve from mystical health-giving potions for an academic elite to a means of common stupefaction.

Throughout the Middle Ages, beer continued to be the people's drink in northern Europe, with mead – a ferment of the most common sweetener, honey – a useful domestic supplement in England. Wine was the everyday drink of Mediterranean lands where the vine flourished (although two successive poor vintages in France, 1151 and 1152, meant that even the French, for the first time in living memory, had to make do with beer and mead). The common people in northern Europe drank wine as part of ritual and celebration, and when it was cheap. (A gallon of Gascon, Rochelle or Rhenish wine, precursors of claret, Loire and Liebfraumilch respectively, was available for as little as four pence a gallon after the bumper vintage of 1394.)

But to noblemen, even in England and even when taxes and unrest made all imports expensive, wine was commonplace. By the fourteenth century, wines from all over France, Germany, Portugal, Spain and Italy were being shipped to England by foreign vintners. The patterns of the international wine trade were therefore so well established that when Henry VIII eventually ordered the dissolution of the monasteries, it heralded a four-century intermission in England's viticultural tradition but by no means left English thirsts unslaked – as witness Shakespeare's frequent references to the powerful wines of southern Iberia: sack, canary and sherris, the precursors of what we know today as sherry.

André Simon's *History of the Wine Trade in England* records the fascinating minutiae of these transactions including, for example, the hundreds of tuns of wine supplied by an Irish justiciary, John Wogan, in 1301 and 1306 to sustain Edward I and his troops in their attempts to quell the Scots. Edward was to die of dysentery on the bleak shores of the Solway Firth in 1307 but doubtless, however weak he felt, he continued to be succoured with wine until he expired. A major factor in the consumption of alcoholic drinks at this time was that they were widely regarded as a much safer, healthier alternative to water.

Nowadays we know that wine contains alcohol and that alcohol has antiseptic properties, but in 1307 hardly anyone other than a handful of Arab alchemist abstainers had ever encountered the most potent ingredient of wine, beer, cider and mead in isolation. One wonders what medieval man and his predecessors thought was responsible for the very distinctive effects of alcoholic drinks.

The first European distillers saw their produce as medicines and, with any luck, elixirs of, if not immortality, then at least longevity. Hence aqua vitae, "water of life", and the host of similarly optimistic names given to spirits the world over. By the fifteenth century, however, their successors had started to make liquids that were designed for drinking, and by 1496 Nuremberg had already forbidden the sale of "distilled waters" on high days and holidays in an effort to stem drunkenness.

Alcohol in distilled form reached England in the sixteenth century, considerably later than it was known, produced and consumed in Ireland – although 200 years earlier, in Edward III's reign, "the marvaylous use and commoditie of burning water even in warres, a little before the joining of batayle, to styr and encourage the souldiours' myndes" had been recommended by the Catalan mystic Ramon Llull. In England, too, it was introduced on the health ticket, most famously in *The Vertuose Boke of Dystyllacyon of the Waters of all maner of Herbes*, published in 1525. This was a fine panegyric for a substance that so usefully "easeth the diseases coming from cold. It giveth also young courage in a person, and causeth him to have a good memory and remembrance. It purifieth the five wits of melancholy and of all uncleanliness, when it is drunk by reason and measure; that is to understand five or six drops in the morning, fasting, with a spoonful of wine ... It comforteth the heart and causeth a body to be merry."

By 1560 distilled or "burnt" wine was becoming more widely available, and books on distillation were as popular as books on wine and health were to be four centuries later. Distilled spirits were still regarded as miraculous in their benefits, as witness the title of one of the most successful of these books, *Newe Jewell of Health*, and a quotation from another: "It sharpeneth wit, it restoreth memori. It maketh men merry and preserveth youth. It putteth away fracins, ring worms, and all spots of the face, etc. It is merveylous [sic] profitable for frantic men and such as be melancholy. It expelleth poyson. The smell thereof burnt, killeth flies and cold creeping beasts." Of all these claims, that regarding memory seems the oddest.

Mother's Ruin

Up to the end of the seventeenth century, the English continued to drink mainly beer, some cider, its pear-based counterpart perry, and mead. For the rich, and for connoisseurs such as Pepys, these were supplemented by a variety of better-quality wines whose provenance, or at least price, usually directly reflected the international alliances and conflicts of the time. After the Methuen Treaty with Portugal of 1703, drinking port and forswearing French wines was the act of a true patriot in England, although the Scots continued to toast the Auld Alliance in claret.

Although there was a long history of importing wine from the areas which now produce port, sherry and other fortified wines, the wines would not and could not have been fortified until alcohol was known and freely available in spirit form. Port was not to be fortified for its voyage north until 1715, although it continued to be drunk throughout the meal as well as after it even in its new, considerably more potent state.

Compared to most other Europeans, including the Irish and Scots who had long been enjoying their own grain-based spirits as well as beer and imported wines, the English were latecomers to strong drink, taking to it at about the same time as they took to another psychoactive substance, caffeine, in the form of coffee and then tea. Spirits had been tried, with little success, as curatives in the plague of 1593, and the Distillers' Company was formally incorporated in London in 1638 (201 years after the Vintners' Company), partly in a vain attempt to stamp out the activities of their many cottage-industry rivals. The first English rivals to imported French brandy were corn- and barley-based ferments which were distilled and, like practically every-thing else made for internal consumption in pre-refrigerator days, often flavoured with herbs and spices.

The real and ruinous change in English drinking habits was set in train at the end of the seventeenth century. Thanks largely to the introduction of a foreign substance, "Geneva" or Dutch gin, by William of Orange, spirits became widely and cheaply available in England and were actively peddled rather than simply dispensed within the family. Heavy duties were imposed on wines imported from the French enemy (although some connoisseurs continued to savour the finesse they found in their favourite, French wines, wine enthusiasts through history demonstrating a reluctance to have their drinking habits dictated by politics). Beer continued to be drunk in great quantity, particularly in the country, simply as a thirst-slaker which was more trustworthy on health grounds than many water sources.

But spirits, and gin in particular because it needed no complicated barrel-ageing, provided a more economical route to oblivion – an escape from London's increasingly cramped and squalid living conditions, as exemplified in the oft-quoted sales pitch noted by Smollett and illustrated by Hogarth: "Drunk for a penny, dead drunk for two-pence, clean straw for nothing" (the straw being provided to soften the drinkers' fall). This was to be the only era in which the dangerously low production costs of distilled spirits – stills were cheaper than the paraphernalia needed for brewing – were to be made so obvious to consumers.

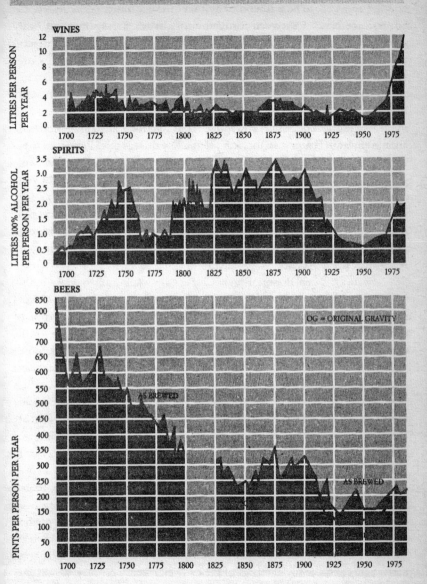

England's first tax on beer had been imposed, not surprisingly, by the Puritan Cromwell, to help fund the Civil War. As consumption increased, so did the eagerness of successive governments to tax it (together with the imported cup that was, in the words of a favourite tea slogan, to cheer rather than inebriate).

And thanks to the records of duties levied by HM Customs & Excise and its antecedents, we have revealing statistics on consumption, or at least licit consumption, from 1684.

As the graph opposite shows, spirit consumption soared in the first half of the eighteenth century, so that in 1726 the Royal College of Physicians was petitioning Parliament about the dangers of excessive drinking in a document remarkably similar to that published by the College 261 years later as *A Great and Growing Evil*, a phrase taken from that original report. The Gin Act, passed in 1736, was in part an answer to the physicians' warnings, but in effect did little to curb consumption. The ordinary Englishman, and many working-class women, had discovered that another, more comfortable, world was theirs for just a few pence.

By 1745, when Bonnie Prince Charlie was leading his troops south-wards, many Sassenachs were in a state of some debilitation. A quarter of Londoners were estimated to be drinking a pint of gin a day. The Hogarthian scenes were inevitably followed by a much more robust attitude to the control and taxation of drinking – although not before one of the world's more important debates on the morality of taxing an activity that some by this stage openly regarded as sinful.

It was indubitably the novelty and alien status of spirits in general, and gin in particular, that made gin seem so much more wicked than the familiar ferments beer and wine to orators such as Lords Chesterfield and Harvey. There was also the fact that gin was quite simply that much more potent (although no more potent than the "burnt wine," or brandy, which Pepys admitted he preferred to ordinary wine in 1667), and that it came to be associated with urban squalor rather than bucolic lubrication.

Drink, drinking and even drunkenness in general were not reviled – were possibly not even a social problem – until the Gin Lane epoch. When Daniel Defoe described someone as "an honest, drunken fellow" he was merely reflecting the social mores of the early eighteenth century, as was Dr Johnson when he observed of his extremely decent birthplace: "All the decent people in Lichfield got drunk every night, and were not worse thought of." This quotation reflects, however, that as the eighteenth century progressed, the age of innocence in the Englishman's affair with alcohol was drawing to a close.

The early Methodist campaigns against the perils of drink were directed almost exclusively at gin and, subsequently, the rum imported from the West Indies. The Methodists were not against alcohol in any form, and John Wesley himself described wine as "one of the noblest cordials".

Even the Puritans had not been against alcohol per se. Increase Mather, perhaps the most important American Puritan ever, preached that "wine is from God". But this enlightened counsel was counterbalanced by the general Puritan view that "the drunkard is from the Devil". In England, the rarely enforced 1606 "Act for Repressing the Odious and Loathsome Sin of Drunkenness" had presumably owed much to the Puritan influence, although alcoholic drinks played a substantial part in their way of life. The *Mayflower* had to stop off in Plymouth, according to the log: "Our victuals having been much spent, especialy our bere". A Dutch distillery was opened on Staten Island as early as 1640, although "Geneva" was to be succeeded by imported rum and then domestic whiskey as the spirit of America.

Alcoholic drinks played an important part in the wider history of colonization: wherever Europeans went, they took the drinks of their culture with them. Thus spread the cultivation of the wine vine to the Americas, the Cape, Australia and New Zealand. (Most French colonies were in areas too hot for successful viticulture, but it was almost as though the British deliberately chose to colonize suitable vineyard land.)

Although brewing techniques of various sorts were already known in most parts of the world, distilled spirits were to be a powerful tool in the process of colonization. These liquors, so much stronger than anything many natives had ever encountered before, were deliberately used to weaken and suppress them while conquering their land. The notorious triangular slave trade, so prevalent in the eighteenth century, started with ships from Bristol or Liverpool loaded with liquor to be traded on the west coast of Africa for Negro slaves, who were shipped in appalling conditions to the West Indies. Much of their place below decks was then occupied on the homeward journey by molasses, to be distilled to finance another voyage around this shameful triangle.

Total alcohol consumption rose steadily throughout the nineteenth century on both sides of the Atlantic. The European-based cultures became cultures of notable consumption of all kinds. Menus of the time make queasy reading today. The English were also introduced to a wide range of spirits, including rum and arrack from the colonies, and some wonderful stuff called whisky which the Scots had previously kept pretty much to themselves. They took to all these new and potent drinks with enthusiasm.

In the 1840s and 1870s, per capita spirit consumption was even higher than in the early disastrous days of cheap gin. Beer was no longer the universal thirst quencher, and per capita consumption of wine had to wait until the late 1970s before reaching the peak levels recorded just before spirits became commonplace in the early eighteenth century. But overall, the Victorians were extremely voracious drinkers. Drink and drinking were fully enmeshed in the fabric of their life. Prosperity meant work, and well-lubricated play, for all.

The quantities drunk during a session were heroic, or at least prodigious. In his *Confessions of an Opium Eater*, Thomas de Quincey, eulogizing the drug of the Orient, observed: "I myself, who have never been a great wine-drinker, used to find that half a dozen glasses of wine advantageously affected the faculties ... " A serious biography of John Mytton, the squire of Halston in Shropshire, records that he drank six bottles of port a day "until he tired of it and changed to brandy".

By the end of the nineteenth century, when he could hardly argue that there was a scarcity of healthy nonalcoholic drinks, the average British adult was downing more than ever: more than two gallons of pure alcohol a year – 30 per cent more than the most recent peak of consumption in 1979.

Even more significant is a comparison of the proportion of total Exchequer receipts represented by the demon drink in Victorian times – up to 40 per cent – and in the late 1970s, about four per cent. Gladstone's libertarian attitude to the drinks trade (reflected in that of the present Conservative regime) paid off quite literally.

The new century, more sober times, World War I and Lloyd George's zeal in keeping alcoholic excess from everyone, and from munitions workers in particular, combined to make Britain's alcohol consumption plummet, although the overall reduction in wine consumption between 1870 and 1920 was effected by a quite unexpected agent: Nature. As though responding to the increasingly strident cries of the temperance movement, first the fungal parasite oidium and then the plant louse phylloxera systematically attacked and devastated the vineyards of Europe and then most of the rest of the world. Wine and therefore brandy production plummeted. It was not until well into the twentieth century that an effective solution (grafting vines on to phylloxera-resistant American rootstocks) was found to this disaster, which threatened for many years to wipe out the world's wine supply.

Lloyd George then showed just how much the State as well as Nature could intervene in citizens' relationship with drink – provided it was prepared to sacrifice considerable pleasure-generated revenue. He even took the brewery closest to one particularly sensitive munitions factory outside Carlisle into state ownership, where it remained for 50 years – an unlikely workplace for civil servants.

Monarchs reflected the spirit of the times. During World War I, King George V had his court give up drink as a measure of austerity and commitment, a sharp contrast to the carousing of his father as Prince of Wales at the end of the previous century. London bars could open only between 6.30 and 9.30pm, although the wily had many ways around this restriction, and those soldiers who made it back on leave must have felt they deserved strong drink as it had never been deserved before.

The official figures, of course, ignore smuggling and illicit home brewing and distilling, so the apparent drops in beer and spirit consumption of 63 and 52 per cent respectively during the Great War may be deceptively dramatic, discouraging as Lloyd George's sharp duty increases were.

Temperance Is Born

For the first time in Britain, it was demonstrated how simply the country's intake of alcohol could be curbed. Measures were brought in which decreed not only that spirits should be sold nearly ten per cent weaker than they had been, but that severe limits should be imposed on the strength of beer, and that drink should be cleared from bond – effectively released for sale – only in carefully rationed amounts.

In *Dear Old Blighty*, E. S. Turner points out that Lloyd George came to regret his famous pledge forswearing consumption of liquor in his own household, and felt in retrospect that he had been made to look a fool. Certainly no one expected "Squiff", the hard-drinking Asquith, to make this supreme sacrifice, and the bars of the House of Commons, which continue to this day to be blithely exempt from the licensing laws, were as busy as ever between 1914 and 1918. When, in 1915, Lloyd George called for much higher duties on spirits, the Hon. Member for South East Cork rose to his feet to plead that while he did not mind what happened to wine duties, his constituents badly needed their whiskey which was essential for women in childbirth. It was also argued that the workhouses desperately needed cheap liquor "to keep alive the poor creatures whose stomachs cannot bear food".

Lloyd George's restrictions on one side of the Atlantic were soon mirrored by much more stringent measures on the other. Total Prohibition was introduced throughout the United States in 1919. The scheme was an event in the social history of drink probably more dramatic than any since Mahomet had outlawed alcohol for millions of people on the other side of the world 12 centuries earlier. (Total Prohibition was also introduced by Finland's new parliamentary regime in the same year.)

One of the many factors that must have encouraged Congress to ratify the 18th Amendment, which allowed one segment of the population to stop another doing something it really loved doing, was America's success in combatting opiate addiction. This had reached serious proportions by the turn of the century – partly because new recruits to the temperance movement were recommended by the medical profession to substitute morphine for the alcohol they now forswore. The 1909 Smoking Opium Exclusion Act may sound far too simple to have worked, but this, backed by harsh West Coast controls on Chinese immigrants, suggested to Americans that the law could be an effective weapon against drugtaking.

Throughout history, drinking has inevitably carried with it the possibility of drinking to excess, and of perils to self and society to which the ancients were by no means blind. Mahomet's ban was particularly strict in that it was introduced at a time when the most potent drink available was only 14 or 15 per cent alcohol. It took the widespread misuse of spirits, about three times as strong as this, to suggest to Western man that alcohol could be a problem as well as a boon, and even then the time scale was notably long.

Major changes in social perception of spirits were needed before they could be seen as a public menace, for these were liquids that had been introduced as an elixir of long and healthy life. This may partly explain the length of the period between the time when cheap gin was freely available and 1804, when the first rumblings of concern about alcohol abuse were heard. In that year two doctors, Thomas Trotter of Edinburgh and Benjamin Rush of Philadelphia, both of whom had trained in Edinburgh, published independently and on each side of the Atlantic treatises outlining the serious medical effects of excessive drinking.

This was a milestone in that drunkenness had previously been seen only as a general social problem, a spur to public disorder, unruliness and what was in some societies called licentiousness. But Trotter and Rush provided evidence that drink caused private, inner, medical harm, too. The temperance movement was born.

The temperance movement began as just that, a group of very sensible and concerned individuals who urged moderation, certainly not abstinence. Like the early Methodists in the previous century, they aimed their sights only at *in*temperance, at excessive drinking and chiefly at spirits.

The opening up of the "Wild" West demanded, or at least fostered, some pretty wild behaviour. In most settlements, the saloon bar was constructed many years before the church and became the focus of such social life as there was, much of it centred on gambling and prostitution. To the upright gentlefolk of the East Coast, the saloon bar with its shots of hard liquor and rough trade of several sorts came to symbolize all that was evil in America. One powerful cohort in the eventual army of sobriety was even called the Anti-Saloon League. (By World War I it had devised a particularly imaginative battle cry, denouncing alcohol as "unAmerican, pro-German, youth-corrupting and treasonable.")

The first temperance society was founded in Saratoga in upstate New York in 1808 but the movement spread rapidly, with an eventual base in Boston: the American Society for the Promotion of Temperance, founded in 1826. Thanks largely to the influence of the fundamentalist churches, the movement had a million members, one in every 12 Americans, by 1833. At this stage it was proposed that those who "signed the pledge" should abstain not just from distilled spirits but from all forms of alcohol, but the proposal was voted out (showing just how differently spirits had been viewed from beer and wine), only to be accepted three years later. One of the first of the American temperance organizations, however, had consisted of a group of men who wined and dined together while they discussed their opposition to intemperance.

The tiny Irish village of Skibbereen is credited with being the seat of the temperance movement in Europe, a small society being founded there in 1818. But it was not until 11 years later that the movement really took hold, chiefly in Northern Ireland and, to a lesser extent, in Scotland, where spirits had, of course, been part of the social fabric for rather longer than in England. The movement worked its way south, so that by the middle of the eighteenth century the British and Foreign Temperance Society numbered bishops and archbishops among its presidents, and could boast Queen Victoria as its patron (although widowhood, it is said, drove her to the heady cocktail mixture of whisky and claret).

Although today we tend to associate a hard line on drinking with hard-line Protestants (the Rev. Ian Paisley was still railing against the evils of allowing Sunday drinking in Ulster in July 1987), the temperance movement embraced worshippers of all ecumenical persuasions. Many churchmen had to reconcile the fundamental role of wine in their religion with this new social movement which viewed all alcohol with revulsion. For Roman Catholics such as the influential Irish temperance campaigner Father Theobald Mathew, whose methods were echoed by Billy Graham a century later, the doctrine of transubstantiation conveniently explained their regular intake of communion wine as participation in the blood of Christ.

These early temperance workers were far from the killjoys they may seem today. In the very different social and historical context of the times, the advocates of abstention in Ireland felt, rather like members of Solidarity in Poland today, that alcohol was being used to manipulate the common people. In the introduction to his eulogy of wine connoisseurship *Stay Me With Flagons* (1940), Maurice Healy described his Irish Catholic childhood: "In the peculiar circumstances of the country in which I was born and grew up it was right that I should have been a teetotaller. Conditions were not normal. An evil political system had produced an evil social system. For hundreds of years a people had been deliberately degraded . . . They were forbidden all forms of culture . . . And wine and all fermented drinks call for culture in their use, else they will be abused. The poor wretch who lifted his heart with a tot of raw home-made Whiskey and for a moment forgot his misery was not to be blamed if he acquired a habit and took to increasing the size of the dram. Drunkenness inevitably followed." As Maurice Healy noted, Father Mathew's slogan was "Ireland sober is Ireland free".

In the United States, the temperance movement was motivated less by the need to purge the awful legacy of history than a desire to purge a new country of what was perceived as sin. This early example of a still-rampant force in the collective American psyche wielded extraordinary power. By 1851, drinks stronger than cider were available only on prescription in the state of Maine, and a further 14 states were to go completely "dry" long before Congress forced them to. The Prohibitionists were, typically, well-established Protestant farming families, who feared the potential power and disruptive influence of the typical city-dwelling, wine-drinking recent immigrant (who must have found it near impossible to see what all the fuss was about). The issue polarized the nation, so that the original gentle aims of encouraging temperance evolved into a harsh confrontation between "wet" and "dry". Moistness was not a condition that was recognized.

The founding of the Women's Christian Temperance Union in 1874 showed that temperance had become one of the first issues on which women took a collective and public stand. The traditional defenders of peaceful home life felt so emotionally agitated by this threat that the movement developed with unprecedented passion and spontaneity. The women's suffrage movement could even be said to have had its roots in the temperance cause, and in the early years of the twentieth century crusaders for votes for women were to become exasperated with those for whom Prohibition was the only motivation.

Indeed, for as long as it has been an issue, alcohol abuse has been one over which "gender wars" are waged. Probably the most seminal, certainly most emotive, anti-alcohol lobby seen in recent years has been America's Mothers Against Drunk Drivers, or MADD. There is no FADD and much of the anger contained in MADD has been directed by women at men. Although the picture is changing rapidly, society as a whole still tends to see excessive drinking as a male sin, visited on women and children in the form of accident, domestic violence and economic privation.

By the early years of this century in the United States, Prohibitionists had become valuable political allies, and the constitutional amendment of 1919 was the fruition of their work to use this as leverage. They were also helped by the fact that temporary Prohibition on brewing and distilling had been imposed during World War I to preserve the country's grain supply.

But Prohibition in the United States and Finland, and the partial Prohibitions which had been introduced elsewhere in Scandinavia, were doomed to failure, none more literally spectacular than in the US. Here the imposition of this tight theoretical control on a young, entrepreneurial, sprawling and far from unified nation arguably set back the cause of lawfulness by several decades. In the West, where there were still gunfights in the streets, and in the South where lynch mobs were still taking the law into their own hands decades after Repeal, the effect of this edict from Washington was somewhat dilute in any case. And in the sophisticated cities of the East, it was a spur to criminal activity and ingenuity.

When Prohibition was introduced, demand for communion wine, for example, skyrocketed. Prohibition was a godsend to the Mafia, laying the foundations of today's distribution system for other drugs, and a boon to those Canadian and British traders who decided to capitalize on the thriving "bootleg" trade by shipping hooch as far as the 12-mile offshore limit. The financial headquarters of the world's largest distilled spirits company, Seagram, is to this day in Montreal rather than New York. Berry Bros, proprietors of the world's most genteel wine shop in St James's Street,

London, and of Cutty Sark Scotch whisky, were able to buy the entire 1933 crop of several top Bordeaux châteaux when they got back to their more mainstream business from profitable dealings in Nassau.

By 1930, the evil saloon bar had been replaced by the even less reputable, and illegal, speakeasy. An estimated 35,000 Americans had been killed by moonshine or other forms of illegal liquor, demonstrating all too powerfully how complicated is the art of distillation and how necessary are controls and supervision of it. The pro-Prohibition faction was in disarray, having been split by ecumenical and ideological infighting. The Repeal formalized in 1933 was inevitable, and considerably accelerated by the economic depression of the early thirties, which reminded America of her pressing need for increased production and excise revenues. Prohibition, which President Hoover had to admit bravely was but a "noble experiment", can now be regarded as just another demonstration that man's need for a mental escape route cannot effectively be legislated against.

In a less constrained social climate, Britain also saw a slump in total per capita alcohol consumption to coincide with the Great Slump, which brought drinking below even World War I levels. World War II brought the practical difficulties of importing wine, but since then our total consumption of alcohol rose fairly steadily, reflecting new and widespread prosperity. The drinking of new sorts of spirits such as Smirnoff and Bacardi and, particularly, of wine more than compensated for a decline in the popularity of beer, the traditional chosen drug of the British proletariat. The notable increase in the amount of alcohol drunk in Britain in 1977, 1978 and 1979 was doubtless a major impetus for the new generation of temperance campaigners, for the recent reports of the medical Royal Colleges on alcohol and, indirectly, for this book.

CHAPTER TEN

An Alcoholic Anthropology

The World In Its Cups

Because attitudes to drink and drinking are shaped by a subtle combination of social mores and pressures imposed by law and the Exchequer, alcohol is seen in a different light in each country, or rather in each legal and fiscal unit. (Each American and Indian state, for instance, imposes widely differing controls on alcohol.) And, of course, even within a single legal and fiscal unit, there can be marked regional variations in drinking habits and attitudes: as between Glasgow and Edinburgh in Scotland, for example, or between the urban wastes of Oakland and, just 30 miles away, Oakville in the heart of California wine country.

Like the historical survey which precedes it, this geographical survey of alcohol and attitudes to it is hardly comprehensive. It does have a noble aim, however: to highlight the more salient features of how other cultures cope with the demon drink. Inebriation itself, for instance, is seen variously in different societies as shameful, hilarious, a sign of virility or an indication of physical weakness. An examination of such differences, hinting the truth that must underly them, helps put our own attitudes and current concerns into perspective and, in some important instances, suggests how we in Britain could learn by example.

In terms of their responses to drink, the nations of the world can be very roughly divided into Mediterranean cultures, Scandinavian or Nordic nations, non-European "Other Drug" cultures such as those in much of

South America, Asia and Third World countries, and the "Old Colonies" such as Australia and New Zealand. British culture has "Mediterranean" and "Scandinavian" elements, but has a unique web of attitudes which to a certain extent form the basis of those in The Old Colonies. Finally, in a class of its own as regards alcohol, North America, the most notable Old Colony of all, is allocated a section of its own in this skim around the world in its cups. The richness of the ethnic cocktail that has gone to make up the United States, and the speed with which it has been mixed, have resulted in an unparalleled complexity in that country's rules, regulations and attitudes to what is regarded there so unequivocally as a demon.

Mediterranean Cultures

Mediterranean countries tend to have the most relaxed, although not necessarily permissive, attitude towards alcohol. This is doubtless largely because it is here that wine is produced in the greatest quantity and has been more or less continuously for millennia – except where forbidden by followers of Islam, such as in North Africa and in parts of the Near East. Not only have those who live around the Mediterranean had a long time to accustom themselves to strong drink, their economies tend to be heavily dependent on wine and, often, distilled wine in the form of brandy.

It is difficult for a society to turn morally against a substance that provides a substantial proportion of its workforce with a living – as France, the world's largest exporter and most enthusiastic consumer of alcoholic drinks, is finding at the moment. The French government has to walk a tightrope between being seen to act responsibly in the current climate of world opinion on alcohol, while not losing the all-important agricultural vote.

The standard Mediterranean response to alcohol and problems associated with it is not so much odd as almost nonexistent. A defensive: "Problems? What problems?" would be less common, at least among older people in southern Italy, Spain and Portugal (an honorary Mediterranean country for the purposes of this section), than utter incomprehension. So enmeshed in Mediterranean society is the ingesting of alcohol in various forms, so "natural" does it seem, that Alcoholics Anonymous is still viewed by many as a concept almost as ludicrous as, say, a support group called Breathers Anonymous.

Mediterranean society is the home of café society. The social life of many Mediterranean villages revolves around the bar or café, where a large proportion of the (male) population apparently sits in daylong communion with his peers and his glass. In many rural Mediterranean areas, no permits are needed to open up a stall selling strong drink. Even in metropolitan Italy, it can be noticeably easier to buy a drink than a packet of cigarettes (no bad thing, perhaps), and in France in 1978 there was a fully licensed bar of some sort for every 234 mouths – compared with one for every 754 in England and Wales.

While social intercourse without alcohol is rare, alcohol with meals has been almost inevitable. While ever more cheap wines were coaxed from the vine-covered plains that skirt the Mediterranean in the sixties and seventies, water supplies have been improved only slowly in many areas. There has therefore been both economic and hygienic encouragement to drink wine simply for its properties as a lubricant rather than intoxicant, or to dose local water with this widely available antiseptic rather than invest in bottled water or other soft drinks. (Less than 20 years ago in Tuscany, with staff meals at one of Italy's most sophisticated hotels, I was offered unlimited free wine but expected to pay if I wanted to drink reliable water.)

Italy produces even more wine than France in some years and has an even longer experience of wine making and drinking, which doubtless helps to explain her insouciance not only towards alcoholism but even connoisseurship. The difficulty with any sort of analysis of Italy, especially one concerning a subject so alien to Italians as the concept of alcohol abuse, is the national statistics famine. International authorities on the cultural aspects of drinking, such as Dr Robin Room of the Alcohol Research Group in Berkeley, California, point out, however, that as the precision of medical reporting in Italy improves, the calculable rate of cirrhosis increases.

It speaks volumes that the standard (and extremely conscientiously compiled) comparative appraisal of national attitudes to drink, *Alcohol in the World of the 80s – Habits, attitudes, preventive policies and voluntary efforts*, is so overwhelmed with statistics from northern Europe that Sweden, for example, merits 12 pages, Finland and Norway eight each and Poland ten, whereas the material available on Italy, Spain, Portugal, Greece, Yugoslavia and Bulgaria *combined* covers a scant six pages – including the bald and somewhat mystified statement: "drunkenness is uncommon in relation to the large consumption". (Most statistics on drinking in Mediterranean countries are doubtless inflated by the enormous quantities downed there each summer by toping visitors from northern Europe, but this phenomenon is probably counterbalanced by the amount of wine produced and consumed so domestically that it escapes the notice of the statisticians. Italy, in particular, specializes in this back-garden sort of wine production.)

Greece is a good model of a culture in which drink is extremely familiar and drunkenness almost unknown. In fact, per capita alcohol consumption in the southern and eastern Mediterranean, in Greece, Bulgaria and Yugoslavia, is relatively low, about the same level as in Britain: the equivalent of around seven litres of pure ethyl alcohol a year. In Greece, the European home of the vine, drunkenness itself is not only unusual but utterly unacceptable to society. A group of Greeks meeting with the express purpose of imbibing strong drink would be as likely as a group meeting to stick pins into each other (or, four centuries ago, a group meeting to stick lighted rolls of dried leaves in their mouths . . .).

Although alcohol is taken by many Greeks most days, it is taken with or immediately after food when its harmful effects are minimized. Very few places exist simply to sell alcoholic drinks in Greece; the places that sell drink usually sell it as an adjunct to the food they serve. The ubiquitous taverna is the equivalent not of a pub but of a restaurant. Greeks regard the "bars" specially contrived to provide foreign tourists with a means of getting drunk as very odd places indeed. Whatever is the purpose of drinking to the point of mindlessness?

At a Greek wedding, for example, even between quite poor families, it is a point of honour for the host to provide limitless quantities of strong drink – to suggest to the groom and his family that he has made a good match. The guests by no means fall on this bounty. They may sip it, and will certainly toast the bridal pair. There will be plenty of dancing and merriment but no one loses control, except possibly the bride's parents in their emotion at seeing her wed.

Compare this with a working-class wedding in Britain. If the bride's family is not well off yet determined to provide some celebration, the most common economy at the wedding reception is the provision of a cash bar in place of any free drink, since the typical Briton responds so irresponsibly to this sort of generosity. But then Britain is not (yet) a wine-drinking culture, has been familiar with alcoholic drinks for several millennia less than the Greeks – and excise duties on drink are considerably higher than in Greece, or indeed any Mediterranean country, where table wine is not usually taxed at all. In Italy, spirits are cheaper, including taxes, than in practically anywhere else in Europe, and even in France the duty on spirits has been hardly half that charged in Britain.

A major difference between Mediterranean and other cultures' attitudes to drink is that alcohol is not invested with such symbolic value, either. To the Greeks and Italians, alcohol is just one substance in the store cupboard. No one has ever tried to rob them of it. They would hardly understand even the concept of a temperance movement. So what's the fuss? Contrast this with the extraordinarily high symbolic value of liquor in the United States during and after Prohibition.

Italy is perhaps the typical Mediterranean culture in its attitude to drink, combining the high per capita consumption of France with the low incidence of drunkenness of Greece. The drunk is seen as a wimp in macho Italy, a fool who doesn't understand how to handle an everyday and unremarkable substance, perhaps because of some physical weakness. Illustrating nicely the thesis that drunks do what different societies expect of them, Italians still rarely associate aggression and violence with drunkenness, although the general move north into the cities is changing this, fast. The typical Italian wants to eat, not drink. How barbaric the drunken hooligan element in British football fans must seem to the Italians and other Mediterranean cultures.

As in most Mediterranean cultures, in Italy wine is by far the most popular form of alcohol and is almost exclusively drunk with meals. Yet just as in those other major wine-drinking countries France and Spain, per capita consumption has been falling as workers move indoors and soft drinks, beer and even water replace wine as the normal thirst quencher (just as reliable water supplies started to replace beer in England three centuries ago). Wine is seen as a peasant drink, for those who cannot afford to indulge in something as smart as a bottle of whisky or who are not emancipated enough to understand the Coca-Cola culture. Whereas wine accounted for 91 per cent of the average Italian intake of pure alcohol in 1950, this proportion had fallen to 71 per cent by 1985.

Mediterranean societies may have much to teach us in their attitudes to drinking to excess, but the exceptionally high total consumption of alcohol notched up in many of them – albeit on the basis of little and often rather than the Nordic oblivion-or-nothing syndrome – is not without its drawbacks. Italian and Portuguese insouciance towards drink means, for example, that there are still no effective legal controls on blood-alcohol levels in drivers in those countries, and little recognition that this might be a bad thing.

A survey conducted in the mid-seventies showed that 43 per cent of French adults drank wine every day. The 1983 league table on page 148 shows the Hungarians, Italians, Austrians, Portuguese and then French have the worst rate of fatal cirrhosis and chronic liver disease in the world (England and Wales having hardly a tenth the rate of Hungary's). Each of these countries is among the world's top dozen consumers of alcohol.

The cirrhosis mortality league table is, of course, dependent on the accuracy and precision of medical reporting. We should not feel too smug ourselves. It is thought that British doctors are, for the purposes of accurate assessment of our national rate of cirrhosis, over-tactful on many of the death certificates they make out. These figures also ignore the actual incidence of cirrhosis and merely take account of those who die from it. The true picture of the incidence of cirrhosis may be affected by different countries' policy on it and resources for treatment.

Nevertheless, there does seem to be some correlation between fatal cirrhosis of the liver and those, largely Mediterranean, countries where wine is consumed regularly. The top three per capita wine consumers, the Portuguese, Italians and French, feature in the five nationalities with the highest cirrhosis and chronic liver disease mortality rate in the world.

This is a very real and current problem for the French, perhaps the archetypal wine producing and consuming nation – although their regional cirrhosis statistics suggest that it is alcohol, and not wine itself, that is the cause. France's highest per capita incidence of cirrhosis mortality is not in any wine region but in the big cities and in Normandy, land of cream, apple tarts, cider and calvados.

Normandy is a long way from the Mediterranean, of course, but for the purposes of this book France, with its wine-based culture, is included in this Mediterranean section. France is also by far the most sophisticated "Mediterranean" country, which means it is not only less isolated from the current climate of opinion about alcohol in northern Europe and the United States, but also has a far better treasury of statistics than, say, Italy, Spain, Portugal or Greece. These show, for example, that cirrhosis was only half as common in France during World War II, when production and consumption of alcoholic drinks plummeted.

They also show how the French are becoming more conscious of the state of the nation's livers and how determinedly they have been trimming their alcohol consumption recently. In 1979 the average Frenchman drank 15.8 litres of pure alcohol. In just six years he (and she) had cut this to 13.9, although this was still more alcohol than any other major nationality imbibed. Contrary to popular belief, the French managed this by cutting down on wine

TOTAL ALCOHOL CONSUMPTION

	TOTAL LITRES OF 100% ALCOHOL	WINE LITRES		SPIRITS LITRES OF 100% ALCOHOL		BEER PINTS	
	1985	85	83	85	83	85	83
FRANCE	13.9	80.0	85.0	2.3	2.5	70.6	76.9
PORTUGAL	13.1	88.0	99.0	0.8	0.8	62.5	67.8
HUNGARY	12.3	24.8	32.5	5.4	4.8	162.6	155.4
SPAIN	11.8	48.0	57.0	3.0	3.0	107.3	102.8
WEST GERMANY	11.3	21.2	26.5	1.8	2.5	256.6	261.0
AUSTRIA	11.1	34.3	37.4	1.5	1.6	196.4	192.5
BELGIUM	10.8	22.7	21.7	2.1	2.2	223.5	225.3
SWITZERLAND	10.8	49.6	48.3	2.1	2.2	123.7	123.7
CZECHOSLOVAKIA	9.9	14.3	13.5	3.4	3.4	230.2	260.1
DENMARK	9.8	20.7	18.9	1.7	1.6	227.0	244.3
ITALY	9.4	80.0	91.4	1.2	1.2	38.2	36.4
AUSTRALIA	9.2	21.2	19.7	1.2	1.2	202.4	217.9
ARGENTINA	8.7	60.1	71.1	1.0	1.0	17.6	16.0
BULGARIA	8.7	22.7	22.6	3.0	3.0	170.3	107.7
NETHERLANDS	8.4	15.0	13.9	2.2	2.6	148.5	147.8
NEW ZEALAND	8.1	14.4	12.8	1.7	1.7	202.0	201.3
CANADA	7.8	9.3	9.9	2.6	3.0	143.1	147.3
USA	7.7	9.0	8.4	2.6	2.9	157.9	161.5
UK	7.1	10.9	9.5	1.7	1.6	191.2	194.3
REP. OF IRELAND	6.9	3.5	3.2	1.8	1.4	191.8	190.1
GREECE	6.8	42.5	45.0	–	–	59.7	50.5
POLAND	6.7	7.9	8.5	4.6	4.1	51.9	48.4
FINLAND	5.9	4.5	8.5	2.8	2.8	108.4	101.0
USSR	5.7	11.6	12.9	3.0	3.3	41.8	42.8
CHILE	5.6	40.0	39.1	–	–	28.2	26.6
YUGOSLAVIA	5.3	26.5	29.0	2.2	2.3	85.9	84.1
SWEDEN	4.8	12.0	10.8	2.0	2.3	81.0	79.2
JAPAN	4.4	0.8	0.8	2.5	2.0	69.7	73.0
SOUTH AFRICA	4.2	9.2	9.6	1.1	1.2	69.3	68.6
NORWAY	4.1	5.1	4.0	1.4	1.3	83.6	79.7
COLOMBIA	2.8	–	–	–	–	98.6	79.2
MEXICO	2.3	0.5	0.3	1.0	1.0	61.6	59.0
BRAZIL	1.4	2.5	2.5	–	–	39.2	33.4

– FIGURES NOT AVAILABLE

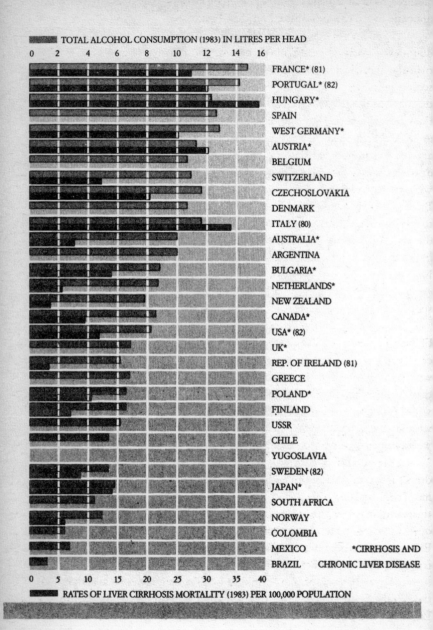

TOTAL ALCOHOL CONSUMPTION (1983) IN LITRES PER HEAD

0	2	4	6	8	10	12	14	16

FRANCE* (81)
PORTUGAL* (82)
HUNGARY*
SPAIN
WEST GERMANY*
AUSTRIA*
BELGIUM
SWITZERLAND
CZECHOSLOVAKIA
DENMARK
ITALY (80)
AUSTRALIA*
ARGENTINA
BULGARIA*
NETHERLANDS*
NEW ZEALAND
CANADA*
USA* (82)
UK*
REP. OF IRELAND (81)
GREECE
POLAND*
FINLAND
USSR
CHILE
YUGOSLAVIA
SWEDEN (82)
JAPAN*
SOUTH AFRICA
NORWAY
COLOMBIA
MEXICO
BRAZIL

*CIRRHOSIS AND CHRONIC LIVER DISEASE

0	5	10	15	20	25	30	35	40

RATES OF LIVER CIRRHOSIS MORTALITY (1983) PER 100,000 POPULATION and spirits almost equally, and beer almost as much. Of the Mediterranean cultures, most of which are cutting down on alcohol, only Spain made a more dramatic move towards abstention than France.

To many foreign visitors, the ubiquity of alcohol in various forms is doubtless a major (if subliminal) part of the charm of rural France. The roadside signs luring passing motorists into *dégustations* and *caveaux* by the score; the bottle shops in the petrol stations; the fully licensed cafés open throughout the day and most of the night: these are facts of life which the French hardly notice but cannot fail to strike those who come from cultures in which alcohol is viewed and taken less casually. Many foreigners are amazed to see how early in the day many Frenchmen appear to start their drinking: a *café-calva(dos)* for breakfast, a pastis at 10 being quite *normale*, along with truck drivers whose midday alcoholic intake seems to exceed the average British labourer's on a Friday night. The language itself provides many clues to traditional attitudes. Liquor after a meal is drunk merely as a *digestif* to help digestion or as a *pousse-café* or coffee-pusher. The glass of calvados often drunk in the middle of a meal in Normandy is merely filling the *trou Normand*, or Norman hole. A hangover makes no reference to its cause and is simply a *gueule de bois*, or "wooden mouth". And it is surely significant that any non-specific short-term malaise is known as a *crise de foie*, or "liver crisis".

So enmeshed is the production and consumption of alcoholic drinks in French life that not only are taxes on domestically produced drinks minimal or extremely low, but there are, for example, still nearly a million fruit farmers who are allowed to distil their own spirits, averaging a production of more than 20 litres of pure alcohol each a year – the equivalent of about a bottle a week. And a special law was needed to try to ensure that the lunchtime wine without which most teachers would have found it difficult to function is kept well away from the pupils themselves.

Yet all this is changing. In France today, the *boisson* (nonalcoholic drink) is steadily taking over from the *consommation* (alcoholic drink). The more sophisticated, urban French are much more careful about monitoring their drinking habits than their British counterparts. Despite the snob value of *le Scotch*, they are extremely wary of spirits, and except in a handful of Parisian wine bars haunted mainly by foreigners, drinking wine without food is regarded as bizarre behaviour.

To any French person, drinking is still essentially a male activity (although the figures suggest that this is changing among the young). And to a Parisian, drunkenness is associated with the poor, the provinces, some sports (notably *le rugby*), and foreigners unused to the drinking possibilities that exist in France. There is no French equivalent of the drunken English "Hooray Henry" or Lager lout, and as in every other Mediterranean country there is not a jot of shame, even among young bloods, in choosing not to drink alcohol in a social setting.

In the countryside things are changing too, but more slowly. The French still love to eat, and they know that their food tastes even better with wine than without. This means that a lot of alcohol is ingested as mere lubrication, and often, given the setting of a high proportion of French restaurants and banquets, by those who then take to the wheel of a car. In 1980, alcohol was generally considered to be an important factor in between 40 and 45 per cent of all road accidents. The random "alcotest", equivalent to the Breathalyzer, is slowly taking effect, after much public uproar (and an attempt at exemption on professional grounds from wine brokers in Bordeaux), with maximum blood-alcohol levels the same as in Britain.

Seminal in French contemporary thought on alcohol was a 1980 report commissioned by Giscard d'Estaing from Professor Jean Bernard which, for the first time, proposed a national policy on alcohol, to be introduced to the wary French in gentle stages over ten years. Chief among Bernard's recommendations was that France's welter of worthy laws on drink – including such gems as that parents should not give their children strong drink undiluted – should actually be enforced. (At the moment, beer and wine may publicly be served, undiluted, to anyone over 13.)

The report also proposed lowering the alcohol content of many drinks, notably through an end to wine chaptalization. (The EEC authorities are rather keen on continuing chaptalization, although adding concentrated grape sugar to fermenting grape juice, in place of beet sugar, to make the resulting wine stronger, as a way of helping drain the European wine lake ...) Professor Bernard's proposals included a serious programme of educating young people on alcohol and, what the drinks producers dreaded, that prices should be raised to deter consumption and that there should be greater controls on advertising.

Television advertising of strong drink has become a surprisingly emotive issue in a country that embraces roadside sampling and the selling of it at filling stations. In June 1987, a huge row blew up about the advertising on television of something as innocuous as a low-strength beer – perhaps because it was on a channel owned until recently by the government, now associated with a holier-than-thou attitude towards alcohol.

If anyone has ever felt like starting a temperance movement in France, they certainly never got very far with it. There is a national organization for dealing with alcoholism, and the counselling centres it operates offer, with inspired euphemism, *Consultations d'hygiene alimentaire*.

Just like its counterparts in most of the rest of the Mediterranean, the French bloodstream seems to expect a constant topping up of its alcohol content. Wild excesses of behaviour under the influence may be uncommon, but so is complete sobriety. All of those who drink in France's myriad cafés and bars may do so in the shadow of a notice which officially demands the *Protection des Mineurs et Répression de l'Ivresse Publique* (Protection of Minors and Repression of Public Drunkenness), but in which other country would you find a marathon route punctuated with medically approved "wine stops", as in the Bordeaux Marathon, 1986 and 1987?

The Nordic Influence

A Nordic drinker in a Mediterranean setting is a wonder to behold. Many of them, such as the Norwegian poet I once knew in Provence, seem uncomfortable with the forbidden fruit hanging from every tree, giving the impression that they'd find the vice-like controls on liquor sales so familiar back home almost easier to cope with than the responsibilities of personal freedom. On those, non-ode, days on which Lief allowed himself to drink, his eyes would roll in lascivious but appalled anticipation as he laid in the precise quantity of bottles he calculated would do the trick. He'd shake his head at them, saying proudly, "Oh, I'm going to feel terrible tomorrow morning." If the southern generalization is little and often, the northern one is oblivion or nothing.

Comparison of attitudes to drink and drinking in the deep south and far north of Europe suggests there may be some arcane but direct relationship between alcohol and sunlight. In Greenland, for example, alcohol dependence has overtaken tuberculosis as the nation's greatest health hazard. And it may even be that television, that other opiate of the masses in darkness, may play a part in the equation. When Thursdays in Iceland, for instance, were the nation's television-free day, the Icelandic police force had apparently to work overtime on the consequences of the national weekly peak in drinking. It is a cliché that the Scandinavian attacks his drink with diligence rather than gusto, but a cliché with a great deal of truth in it. In stereotypically liberal Sweden, drinking is an activity overloaded with moral significance.

With the exception of those master brewers to the world, the Danes, however, the Nordic people and even the much-maligned Poles and Soviet citizens do not drink a great deal when their consumption is averaged out per capita over a year. (For the purposes of this brief appraisal, Poles and Russians are included with more obviously Nordic races, although it has to be remembered that a fifth of the Soviet population is Muslim and therefore forbidden alcohol.) In the league table of alcohol intake per head, Poland, Finland, the USSR, Sweden, Iceland and Norway – in that order – are all below the United Kingdom (although these official statistics should be seen in the light of the rumour that in Norway, for example, more alcohol is distilled illegally than legally). When the typical northerner does decide to drink, however, he does it with such little control. This is binge territory. Here the psychology, if not the practising rites, of Lutheranism are strong after all. And there are few more powerful illustrations of personal accountability than a hangover.

In most of the territory under examination here, spirits are the favoured drink, providing a far more direct route to oblivion than wine or beer. Despite their sober performance in the league table of total alcohol consumption, Poland, the USSR and Finland are in the world's top ten spirits drinkers. The climate is too cool to grow vines so beer rather than wine is the indigenous ferment, although it is often drunk with, rather than (more wisely) instead of, spirits.

The favoured spirits in this part of the world are colourless, often relatively tasteless, distillates of grain-based ferments, akvavit, schnapps and vodka being typical. In contrast to, say, the Frenchman's attitude to his "apéritif" Scotch or "digestif" cognac, these neutral spirits are often taken without any supporting framework of connoisseurship or even appreciation of flavour, but rather as drugs, straightforward doses of which are necessary on the route to a different state of mind.

The medical consequences of taking one's alcohol in short, sharp, strong doses rather than on the Mediterranean topping-up principle are interesting. Whereas cirrhosis is the big drink-related health hazard in southern Europe, and in Denmark where drinking habits are in many ways Mediterranean except that beer is substituted for wine, in Nordic countries the nation's drink-related problems are more dramatic. Deaths by acute alcohol poisoning are noticeably more common in these hard spirit-drinking nations than elsewhere.

In Finland in 1984, for example, no fewer than 274 people died by simply drinking themselves to death, whereas in Denmark, with its slightly higher population, the comparable figure for deaths by acute alcohol poisoning was only 50. And visitors to Nordic countries in general, and Finland in particular, are frequently struck by evidence well this side of the ultimate oblivion: public drunkenness of even quite young girls is quite a common phenomenon, notably at the weekend and in the winter in this land of all-or-nothing drinking. Finland's state-controlled liquor stores (each called simply "Alko") have traditionally been closed at weekends during the midnight-sun months of May to September, when many Finns may be engaged in healthier pursuits. As long ago as 1977, the Finnish rate of arrests for drunkenness was up to nearly seven per cent of all adults: a record for Europe and five times higher than in any other Scandinavian country.

Closer to the North Pole, in Iceland, it has been calculated that drinking is even more serious and more concentrated, supporting the alcohol-daylight hypothesis. A survey of drinking habits in the Nordic capitals showed that the median amount of alcohol consumed per head in a Reykjavik drinking session was way above that in Helsinki, and three times that in Stockholm, Oslo or Copenhagen.

The contrast in the incidence of acute alcohol poisoning between freewheeling Denmark and the more restrictive Nordic nations is often cited as evidence that too-stringent controls on alcohol sale and supply are counter-productive. It is certainly true that the state monopoly systems that dribble out liquor in Sweden and Finland could do nothing more to feed the prevailing notion that guilt must necessarily be associated with pleasure in any form, and particularly in the form against which vigorous national temperance movements have railed so loudly. Norway and Finland have each experimented with prohibition in their time, and even today it is quite difficult for many Scandinavians to buy alcoholic drink at all. In Sweden and Finland, there is one shop selling wines and spirits (controlled with full civil-service bureaucracy) for every 26,000 and 23,000 inhabitants respectively. The comparable figure in Denmark, as far as can be calculated in a country where no licence at all is needed to sell liquor, is one for every 300 Danes.

The casual appearance and brazen commercialism of Denmark's liquor stores contrast markedly with the grimly antiseptic atmosphere of Sweden's drink shops. Here staff dress solemnly in white coats to dispense bottles wrapped in brown paper, no bottles are on display or even promoted, and the shops are closed at weekends. One of the Swedish drinker's most valuable works of literature is the thin pamphlet that details exactly the opening hours of each of the state alcohol monopoly's outlets. And once the drinker has managed to gain entry to such a place, he will be expected to pay about £18 for a bottle of spirits. It is hardly surprising that "booze cruising" to Denmark is such a popular pastime, or that illegal distillation is so covertly commonplace in the more remote corners of Scandinavia.

Restrictions on availability and advertising may be two obvious ways of attempting to control alcohol consumption north of Copenhagen, but the exceptionally high duties on drink are probably even more effective. The international sales force of Beefeater gin, a farflung lot, used to have an annual contest to find the world's most expensive gin and tonic. Stockholm's smartest hotel won every time. By 1980, the duty on a standard bottle of spirits had reached 70 Öre, or £7 *plus* 50 per cent of the VAT-exclusive price (the comparable British figure was about £3.50 per bottle).

State-induced restrictions on the available choice and even, in some cases, on the quantity of drink bought seem ferocious to those reared in more tolerant social climates. In at least one respect, however, most Scandinavian countries have an enviable record in coping with alcohol: drunken driving. In Sweden, for example, the percentage of drivers killed in road accidents whose blood-alcohol level is over the statutory limit is only about ten, compared with 30 per cent in England and 40 to 45 per cent in France – even though (or perhaps because?) the statutory limit is much lower in Sweden. The Swedes, in particular, with their notable capacity for making social improvements on a communal basis, were one of the first nations to come to grips with the behavioural changes needed to ensure that drunks did not take to the wheel. In Britain, husband and wife bicker over the cheese course about who's driving home from a dinner party. In Sweden, each party has its "designated driver", a title surely entirely free of wimpishness, decided well in advance.

In Norway and Sweden, at least, efforts to combat drunkenness are in general made on a more communal basis than anywhere else in the world. Each community has its own Temperance Board to which people with alcohol problems are referred, and official statistics paint an impressive picture in which the number of referrals has dropped dramatically (although this could be partly because they've given up on some cases). Norway has a particularly good record of education on alcohol, which has been part of the school curriculum since 1890 (thanks to the pressure from Norway's powerful temperance groups). Today, action on alcohol problems is often undertaken in conjunction with education on other forms of drug abuse, and there is even a government division, sounding ripe for some Ibsen successor, called the Department of Sobriety.

Comparison between liberal Denmark and the other Nordic nations is often used to provide an insight into the effect on public health of different social attitudes to drink. It is revealing that in strict terms of the likelihood of dying through alcohol consumption in either regime, it appears to make very little difference. For while Denmark has a much lower rate of acute alcohol poisoning than more restrictive Finland, fatal liver cirrhosis is compensatingly much more common in Denmark, according to recent figures. These countries at least provide good evidence of a direct correlation between the little-and-often theory of drinking and the incidence of cirrhosis.

The USSR and Poland are, of course, very different from Scandinavia in so many ways, and provide rich source material for anyone studying the relationship between alcohol supply and political power. Throughout Russian history, such has been the nation's enthusiasm for strong drink that those allowed to sell it have been those with real clout. Serfs would remain serfs if they were kept inebriated, and one early attempt to suppress the Soviet Jewry was simply to forbid them to sell alcohol. More recently, Dr Richard Smith contributed a fascinating paper to the *British Medical Journal* on the dramatic role played by alcohol in the rise of the Solidarity movement in Poland. Solidarity, as well as the Communist Party and the Polish government, claimed to be the party of moderation, even going as far as imposing total prohibition, in their attempts to dissociate themselves from the mob drunkenness that has for centuries dogged real social progress in this part of the world – like Scandinavia, a cold, dark corner in winter from which alcohol can provide a particularly alluring escape.

More recently still, we have seen how strong is the Soviet need to drink – and not just to drink but to get drunk, for which spirits are generally needed. Mr Gorbachev's campaign, introduced in 1985, to curb vodka drinking, and in particular drunkenness at work (a common phenomenon in the USSR), has already had dramatic effects. Officially, consumption of vodka fell from 2,565 million litres in 1984 (more than two-thirds of the world's total vodka consumption) to 1,386 million litres in 1986 (hardly a half). This apparent decrease in consumption has brought with it a corresponding increase in ingenuity, however. Evidence suggests that production of *samogon*, or moonshine (in which sugar is a key ingredient), is at an all-time high, the evidence being the empty sugar shelves in so many Soviet grocery stores. In 1987 more than 11,000 Russians died after drinking illegal *Samogon* and 397,000 were charged with making it.

It is also significant that Mr Gorbachev's new institute designed to study Soviet alcohol problems has about 350 members, more than the entire British and American alcohol research teams combined.

Third World

Non-European civilizations have traditionally favoured drugs other than alcohol. Early South American paintings show coca chewing as standard practice in the Andes as long ago as AD500. The Amerindians' enthusiasm for the hallucinogenic effects of the mescal bean is probably more than 10,000 years old. The peyotl cactus was as important to the Aztecs as coca was to the Incas.

Opium was mentioned by Aristotle, Hippocrates, Livy, Ovid, Pliny the Elder and Virgil, as well as in the ancient writings of Egypt, Mesopotamia, Persia and China, and its narcotic effects were as much savoured by the court of the Mogul empire as by thousands throughout India and Iran today. The leaf stimulant khat has been an Arab pharmaceutical for more than 700 years and is still chewed by several millions of East Africans and Arabs.

But chewing khat is a minority activity compared with the use of cannabis in its various forms, as its colourful terminology suggests. An estimated 200 to 250 million people, notably in Africa and Asia, indulge in marijuana, hashish, ganja, pot, grass, kif, dope, bhang, Indian hemp, weed, draw, blow, shit, Mary Jane, Bob Hope and their close relatives.

Alcohol is very much a secondary drug in many parts of this world. Islam and Hinduism, for example, condemn alcohol but condone opium and cannabis to a certain extent. The Hindu parties in India are committed to extend total prohibition from selected states to the whole country, and as recently as 1977 official estimates reckoned that 42 per cent of Indian men and 98 per cent of Indian women had never tasted alcohol. This study presumably took into account the flourishing and often lethal business of domestic distillation and brewing in this tightly controlled social environment for drinking.

The Indians must have found the enthusiastic gin-swilling of their colonists hard to take, particularly since, in the complicated caste system of the dominant religion, Hinduism, alcohol is the drug of the lower classes (cannabis being the preferred and often religiously prescribed drug of the higher castes). To many middle-class Indians, drinking has equalled degradation, although the continuing process of "internationalization", in which predominantly European/American values are superimposed on the rest of the world, has exposed the upper classes, like those of many other Third World nations, to the notion of drinking as a sophisticated sport.

It is interesting, and salutory, to note that the anti-alcohol argument in India has been fuelled not by the personal health considerations that preoccupy the pampered Westerner, but by the suggestion that it is irresponsible to divert much-needed cereals into alcoholic drink production. Another distinguishing mark of attitudes in India (and Pakistan, where alcohol is banned completely by Islam) is the typically hospitable provision of a much more liberal set of regulations permitting alcohol consumption by foreigners.

Buddhism, on the other hand, the dominant religion farther east, has no consistent policy towards alcohol. In Japan, for example, public drunkenness is not only tolerated in businessmen in certain settings, it is actually expected of them and constitutes approved conduct. Ritual is as important in the communal progress to inebriation in the bars of Tokyo and Osaka as in the drinking of sake, the national rice-based ferment, throughout the country. Drunkenness is a major feature in Japanese literature, and there are virtually no controls on drink apart from on drinking and driving. You may not officially drink before you are 20, but strong drink can be bought from automatic vending machines, for which a "closing time" was introduced in 1980 – from 11pm to 5am. The alcoholic drinks industry is economically important to Japan, employing a higher proportion of its workforce than in any country other than France.

Oriental cultures have traditionally been unenthusiastic about grape-based wine, however suitable much of the territory may be for the wine vine. Many Orientals, and indeed American Indians, experience a phenomenon known as face-flushing when they drink. Their faces go bright red and, although it may not put them off drink completely, there is evidence that the face-flushers among Japanese Americans do actually drink less than their peers whose complexions remain unaffected. Such an uncomfortable sensation being common among Chinese, it is hardly surprising that their average per capita alcohol consumption is not particularly high.

Spirits consumption is prodigious, however, among that (relatively small and almost exclusively male) sector of the Oriental community that does drink. A bottle of brandy or whisky is consumed at the table with meals in place of the European bottle of wine. But the Far East in general, and Japan, Hong Kong and Singapore in particular, remain extremely lucrative markets for the cognac producers. Expensive bottlings are specially produced for what they call the "gift market".

In large parts of Asia, alcohol is forbidden completely, usually because of the countries' adherence to Islam. The ingenuity of the many Europeans working in the Middle East, Saudi Arabia and Kuwait, in particular, has been tested by stringent efforts to control the consumption and domestic production of alcohol. Drinking has traditionally been an important component in

European expatriate life, historically encouraged even in young women for its supposed effects in warding off disease. In the sanitized, air-conditioned quarters of visiting workers in Riyadh and Jeddah, that argument no longer holds. These expatriates may not be physically dependent on alcohol, but it demonstrates how strongly it is woven into the fabric of European (and American) social life that so many of them are prepared to risk lengthy imprisonment and deportation to consume it. They can but be encouraged by the rumours of the role played by alcohol in the lives of many high-ranking Saudis.

Even the most fundamentalist Arab countries may not be as "dry" as they appear. On the streets of Iran today, all women are swathed in decorous robes, their faces covered, and the men are apparently devout followers of the Ayatollah Khomeini. There are many closed doors, however, behind which Scotch whisky is sipped by heavily made-up women in miniskirts.

Similarly, in the Muslim parts of Africa, it is not necessarily the case that alcohol is unknown, simply that rather less of it is consumed than in the rest of this alcoholically unsophisticated continent, in much of which fermentable raw material is also far too precious to transform into alcohol. Native ferments, based on cereals, bananas and palm, have been consumed for centuries throughout Africa – often as part of religious ritual. Stronger drink was introduced by Europeans, and in many areas remained in place of more conventional currency from the slave-trading era until quite recently. At the turn of the century, in that vigorous trading nation Nigeria, for example, rich African merchants would store gin rather than gold.

Mirroring the pattern elsewhere in the Third World, the consumption of traditional native beers is a ritualized, communal activity, whereas "imported" (or distilled under licence) stronger drinks come with no social code of moderation. They arrive instead backed by advertising campaigns cunningly associating them with improved "modern" living standards, providing a rare chance of expansion – and high profit margins – for the multinational drinks corporations. In 1981, for instance, Guinness's activities in Africa and Asia represented only 15 per cent of sales, but no less than 36 per cent of the company's profits. The World Health Organization has made much of its concern that the health of the Third World nations should not be jeopardized for the sake of the shareholders of those, relatively few, multinational conglomerates who wield real power in the international drinks business. In underdeveloped nations, where families have to function without such safety nets as social security payments, alcoholism in one parent can endanger the survival of the whole family.

European alcoholic drinks and drinking habits have penetrated Latin America much more effectively than Africa, chiefly because of the much more penetrating level of colonization achieved by the Spaniards and Portuguese from the sixteenth century onwards. Latin America has had a rich history of drug use, notably with stimulants and hallucinogens, but local low-alcohol ferments were also known, and their consumption carefully controlled by religious ritual. Even more shamelessly than elsewhere, drink in the stronger form of wine and eventually spirits was used by the European colonists to subdue and even recruit the native Indians. When the Spaniards and Portuguese settled in Latin America themselves, they brought with them their own (and their church's) tolerant attitude towards alcohol and, particularly to what are now Argentina and Chile, their expertise in wine production.

The result is that those cultures in which the richest diversity of drugs is fully enmeshed are mainly to be found in South America. This is not to say that Latin Americans are necessarily enormous drinkers, but alcohol is very freely available. Argentina, being one of the world's most prodigious producers of wine, not unnaturally also consumes it enthusiastically. Per capita consumption there is higher than anywhere other than Italy, Portugal and France, and according to the most recent figures available, published in *Alcohol in the World of the 80s* (1982), the cirrhosis mortality rate in Argentina was even higher than in France. With the exception of the two major South American wine-producing nations, most Latin Americans consume only moderate amounts of alcohol. Drinking tends to be associated with machismo, however, with the result that what is drunk is drunk by relatively few, predominantly male, quite heavy drinkers. Alcoholics Anonymous has since taken off in South America.

Mediterranean habits transplanted to much of South and Central America seem to have taken on an interesting twist of social obligation. One aspect of drinking, which still, admittedly, plays a part in the poorer sectors of Mediterranean society, is paramount in Latin America. Although there are the same liberal attitudes to the availability of alcohol, especially to children, drinking is not – as in France, for example – associated with gastronomy and connoisseurship, but has become instead a symbol of manhood. While it is unusual for women to drink in public at all, it is socially difficult for a man to refuse a drink, impolite in the extreme not to offer one, and a great honour to pay for one or, preferably, a substantial round of them. Drinking, often wild drinking, is a substantive part of the festivals and carnivals that punctuate the calendar in many South American countries.

As a final illustration of the prevailing social attitudes towards alcohol, it is perhaps worth quoting here from the section on Latin America in the temperance-funded international survey *Alcohol in the World of the 80s*. "As already mentioned," the report concludes wearily, "the Roman Catholic Church has not been a very active force for temperance promotion or for a restrictive alcohol control policy. The Protestant churches, however, have had a large proportion of total abstainers in their ranks. In view of the prevailing attitude towards alcohol, it has required great firmness on their part to adhere to the principle of total abstinence."

The Other "Colonies"

Alcohol playing such a vital part in the process of colonization, it is hardly surprising that it has always been so important to life in the most British of the British colonies: Australia, New Zealand and South Africa.

The first convict ships, loaded to the gunnels with human products of England's Gin Lane era, were well provisioned with rum. In his description in *The Fatal Shore* of the original consumer goods arriving in Sydney Harbour, Robert Hughes writes: "The chief of these was rum, the social anaesthetic and real currency of early New South Wales. Colonial Sydney was a drunken society from top to bottom. Men and women drank with a desperate, addicted, quarrelsome single-mindedness. Every drop of their tipple had to be imported." Hardly surprising, then, that the ruling (regimental) class in early Australian history was known as the Rum Corps. Even today, to the outsider at least, the Australian economy appears to revolve around brewing.

Australia and New Zealand have long had a powerful thirst for beer which has boosted their per capita alcohol consumption well above British levels, and since the early 1970s wine drinking has become a popular sport even for the most aggressively male sector of the Australian population. This was partly thanks to domestic wine's blissfully untaxed state in Australia until 1984. Premier Malcolm Fraser had been a keen wine connoisseur himself, and the Australian wine lobby wielded considerable power during his reign. Things have since changed, but even now taxes on alcohol are relatively low, and the drinks industry there is one of the least tightly controlled.

Drinkers are typically male, regular and thirsty. The national average intake appears to be swelled by a high proportion of heavy drinkers – the pub (a.k.a. "hotel" in Australia) devotees – for the proportion of total abstainers is also high, perhaps as much as 20 per cent (although still considerably lower than in the United States). That the cirrhosis mortality rate in Australia is not particularly high also supports this theory, since cirrhosis tends to be associated with widespread little-and-often drinking.

Recently, however, even Australia has started to become aware that alcohol may bring some problems with it. Of course, for two centuries Australians have had the extremely good excuse for drinking of sheer thirst quenching in the country's often hot and arid climate. But the mid-1980s have seen many drinkers enthusiastically turning from wine and beer to "coolers" much lower in alcohol, just as their counterparts in the climatically similar parts of the USA such as California have done. This suggests that, if drinkers are offered a low-alcohol substitute of an acceptable quality at an acceptable price (which British wine drinkers are not), they will embrace it. It also hints, interestingly, that it is not the alcohol per se that many drinkers crave, but the ethos of a "sophisticated" drink that does not exclude them from the club of drinkers. (In Europe, coolers have not so far succeeded, perhaps because they are too expensive in northern Europe and wine is too cheap in the south.)

A fiscal change in the way that business entertaining is regarded has cut lunchtime drinking dramatically in Australia, but the country's most effective social change in its attitude to alcohol has been the introduction of random breath tests on the roads. The results have been impressive, and suggest that this may be one of the most effective ways in which a country can reform social behaviour in one potentially lethal aspect of living with alcohol. The scheme has been grudgingly embraced by the populace, and in New South Wales alone is calculated to be saving well over A$100 million a year in medical costs and welfare payments.

If anything, New Zealand's attitude to "grog", as it is known in the Antipodes, is even more robust than Australia's. New Zealanders certainly drink more spirits, perhaps a reflection of the Scottish influence (and long winter nights), and only nine per cent of the population are total abstainers. Until 1967, when the pub licensing hours were extended into the evening, this was the land of "the six o'clock swill", when men would struggle to down as much grog as possible in the hour between work and closing time.

Although the emancipation of New Zealand's wine, gastronomy (and women) has brought civilizing changes, drinking is still very much associated with machismo. But whereas the Latin American male will use drink to prove his solvency, his Kiwi counterpart apparently uses it to prove his porosity. He who drinks most wins. One medical researcher who studied male drinking rituals over 18 months isolated 43 different drinking games in a single province. The rugby club is alive and well in New Zealand.

Reflecting social attitudes on exactly the opposite side of the world (and therefore some very similar winters), where there is drinking, guilt is never far behind. In stark contrast to Mediterranean peoples, New Zealanders have a high guilt:drink ratio (like the Mediterranean guilt:sex ratio?), for the temperance lobby is strong there. Total Prohibition was nearly voted in earlier this century, and every three years the populace is given a chance to vote on the issue (about 20 per cent are for it). Whole suburbs of the major cities remain "dry" and pubs still close all day on Sunday.

The South African record on alcohol is predictably grisly, mirroring even today the practices used by our ancestors to subdue indigenous populations. Until 1962, most blacks were not officially allowed to drink at all. Meanwhile, the "dop system" of paying workers on Cape wine farms at least partly in alcohol, with ensuing health and financial problems, was officially outlawed in the early sixties, but a *Cape Times* editorial as recently as May 1987 suggests that it is far from a thing of the past on the less progressive wine farms. Cape Coloureds, probably as a result of the dop system, uniquely in the world regard beer as a higher-status drink than wine, and have accordingly been turning from wine to beer and whisky as their fortunes have improved and the reality of a cash economy has gradually infiltrated the rural areas.

Beer sales to the black population is an immensely profitable source of income for the South African government, which controls beer halls in the black townships (where these shibbeens have just been legalized). Sales of Zulu beer in Durban, for instance, made so many millions for the local administration that employers were asked to encourage their black workers to drink a couple of litres before starting work.

Drinking is fully integrated into white South African life and per capita consumption has been rising steadily. There are signs of some increasing respect for alcohol among young adults, who have been turning from spirits to wine, but it is difficult to admire the widespread custom of employing others to drive in the evening deliberately to minimize drunken driving when the workforce is so exploited.

North America

In so many aspects of social life, the United States of America is very like Britain. In terms of attitudes to drink, however, the Atlantic represents a perceptible, often baffling, sometimes regrettable divide.

Current American concern, one might almost say preoccupation, with personal health has yielded a crop of worrying medical "discoveries" – the

Fetal Alcohol Syndrome and the link between breast cancer and alcohol are just two examples – to be shipped around the world for consumption by less "advanced" cultures. But America's relationship with alcohol is different not just because its scientific resources put it on the cusp of the future. The real difference lies in the past.

The United States represents by far the largest area of Western civilization to which total prohibition has ever applied. And the 14-year period between the ratification of the Eighteenth Amendment and its Repeal is not only relatively recent – within living memory for millions who have only just qualified as senior citizens. Even more significantly, Prohibition was merely a particularly dramatic symptom of a widely held attitude to drink and drinking that prevails to this day. The temperance movement may have been conceived in Edinburgh, but it was born and grew in the US.

The historical development of the temperance movement is outlined in Chapter Nine, but America lives with it and its legacies today, in sharp contrast to the more relaxed environment in which British drinkers may sup. In Britain, for example, pubs may not always be the most salubrious or, even after the big brewers' refurbishment schemes of the early eighties, most sumptuous meeting places. But at least a pall of shame does not hang over them as it does over so many bars in America, designed specifically to protect the sinners therein from public view. Windows are deliberately shaded, shuttered or even blacked and, inside, lighting is kept to a minimum in many US bars, as though Prohibition were still in force, reinforcing the premise that these are not even meeting places but drinking dens. The typical bar in France may be aggressively lit by fluorescence, but at least this illumination underscores the bar's function as social centre rather than sin bin for the lone alcohol addict. The word sin is associated quite freely with drink in America. It would be inconceivable that the British government's excise duties on beer, wine and spirits (and tobacco) would be so lightly dubbed a "sin tax" as their American counterparts are.

This reflects a phenomenon unthinkable in Britain. Alcohol is so reviled in certain, sizeable tracts of North America that most of Utah, Kansas and Arkansas, for example, are completely "dry", as was Oklahoma until the 1970s, and many other areas severely curtail opportunities to buy and consume liquor. Nearly 20 out of the 50 states operate a monopoly on shop sales of spirits, and in almost all states the minimum legal drinking age is 21 – extraordinarily high in view of the experience of sex and, often, other drugs notched up by the average American teenager.

Such restrictions do not, of course, mean that no alcohol is consumed in "dry" or "semi-dry" areas, simply that those who want to drink are forced into private clubs (often with less than wholesome reputations), or to drive for miles to the boundary with some less repressive regime, or to consume potentially dangerous illicitly produced drinks. But the paper mills, at least, benefit from American paranoia about drinking. The brown paper bag is the all-American camouflage for outlawed liquor.

For all their guilt about drinking, Americans do not, in fact, consume huge quantities per head. Alaska and New Hampshire are the hardest-drinking states, but the average per capita consumption is now rather less than eight litres of pure alcohol a year, a bit more than in Britain but definitely less than in Australia and New Zealand, a little less than in Canada and far less than the world's major wine producers, the Benelux and Middle Europe. This average has to be seen, however, in the context of the US's exceptionally high proportion of total abstainers, a proportion which rose above 40 per cent of all adults in the 1950s and is still above 30 per cent. Studies in the early eighties suggested that abstention was not such a popular cause among teenagers and young adults then, but the prevailing social climate in which alcohol operates in America has been cooling radically, and subsequent surveys may show a hardening of attitudes to alcohol even among today's teenagers.

After rising steadily in the liberal sixties and seventies, America's per capita consumption of alcohol fell considerably and consistently (unlike ours) in the straitened eighties, by eight per cent between 1981 and 1985. Even before the 1980 peak had been reached, Americans could be seen to be turning against their old ways of drinking straight whiskey and high-alcohol cocktails towards "lighter" spirits (in terms of colour and, sometimes, alcohol) and wine. The glass of Chablis was replacing the three- (dry) martini lunch by the late seventies, but has since been superceded by the virtuous glass of Perrier water. An informed estimate puts the proportion of New York business lunches at which alcohol is currently served as low as ten per cent – a marked contrast to any comparable figure in London, Paris, Milan, Sydney or just about anywhere else in the drinking world. And when someone opened a bar in Beverly Hills stocking nothing but a sobering range of the world's mineral waters, some felt the writing was on the wall for alcohol in any form.

Of course, a society of 240 million inhabitants is far from homogenous, but the discernible trend is, for the moment at least, very definitely against alcohol and particularly against distilled spirits or "hard liquor", on which Congress raised (the pretty low) taxes by 19 per cent in 1985.

America has traditionally been a beer-drinking nation, and still spends more than half its budget for alcoholic drinks on this relatively dilute form. Thanks to an elevation of beer drinking to an act of connoisseurship in some quarters, through providing the American consumer with a bewildering array of domestic and imported beers, and perhaps thanks to a number of former spirits drinkers who have turned from distillates to brews, beer sales have withstood America's stricter view of alcohol quite well. But the real beneficiaries have been fizzy soft drinks, fruit juices and a brand new generation of drinks which are themselves called coolers, echoing the current American climate for alcohol.

These carefully marketed mixtures of wine, carbon dioxide and soft drinks (which could presumably be made perfectly well in the home or bar without the expensive intervention of a large drinks company) are between two and seven per cent alcohol (considerably below the nine per cent US minimum for anything the law is prepared to call "wine"). They had not even been hatched in 1981, but by 1986 the cooler producers had sold 636 million litres, compared with 1,764 million litres of that alcoholic drink hatched in pre-history, wine. The wine-producing state of California and some connoisseur and still-Mediterranean subgroups apart, wine has never really caught on in the US.

Coolers, on the other hand, are drunk by a wide cross-section of consumers. Although they sell primarily to teenagers and women, they clearly represent to many different people and in many different sorts of social situation a brush with alcohol in a form that is perfectly acceptable to the moral athletes of contemporary America.

It was, perhaps, inevitable that America would start to turn against alcohol as the nation turned from communal consciousness-raising to body-building, but the trend has been accelerated by several factors, some of them unknown on our side of the Atlantic.

One of these is an intriguing direct consequence of the private health business in the US, combined with the appetite of the average American for the sort of dramatic human confrontation that is so alien to the stiff-lipped Brit. In the worthy seventies there was a dramatic increase in the number of treatment centres for alcohol and other drug-abuse problems – indeed, these were often used instead of more obviously penal corrective facilities by the judiciary. The Federal funds put towards such a worthy but hardly mainline cause have since been severely cut back, but too late to stop a wave of expansion which in one year increased the number of such centres from 4,200 to 7,000. This means that some of these rehabilitation centres have been dangerously short of customers, and have spent considerable sums of money actively touting for business.

Cleverly, they tend to target not the supposed alcoholic, alcohol abuser, person who is alcohol dependent (the minefield of terminology is considered elsewhere) but a close relative, particularly child, often female child. The "alcoholic" is then confronted by a process that may range from much-needed action to what must seem like horrifying intrusion and has now earned its own title, "family intervention", whereby, as Elizabeth Taylor put it in an interview with Helen Gurley Brown, founder of *Cosmopolitan* magazine, "They all preface their remarks with the fact they love you and that's why they're doing this and then comes the knuckle sandwich".

The knuckle sandwich is the commitment of the alcoholic to "detox" in somewhere like the much-publicized Betty Ford Centre, as well, of course, as the commitment of many private health-insurance dollars to its administration. Since the early eighties, it has become fashionable to confess to past but now reviled excesses of drugs of all sorts. Graduates from the clinics have been eager to spread word of their moral cleanout – on the nation's potent chat shows if they are famous. And it would not be too farfetched to suggest that by the mid-eighties Betty Ford had become more famous, through her work detoxing the stars, than her husband, once President of the United States. (The most recent incumbent of the White House, meanwhile, found himself with the difficult job of pleasing both the anti-alcohol campaigners and the wine lobby in his adoptive state, California.)

It has not been just the advertisements of the treatment centres that have been aimed at the children of supposed alcohol abusers. Such media coverage and literature on how alcohol affects individuals as is available to the general American public tends to be aimed at the spouse or child of the abuser, or at least at someone who can assume moral superiority over the abuser, rather than the abuser himself. Arguably even more than the British, the Americans enjoy the morally bracing opportunity to wag a finger at a sinner. The speed with which the nation pounced on the case of one young pregnant Californian accused, in 1986, of risking the health of her unborn baby by indulging in sex and drugs against doctor's orders was chilling.

The definition of the Fetal Alcohol Syndrome in the seventies, which associated specific damage to babies with drinking during pregnancy, provided an ideal opportunity for one half of the population to reprove the other. Feelings ran so high that in 1981 the US Surgeon General felt moved to advise all pregnant women to abstain from alcohol entirely, inflicting a whole new series of guilts on the American female. More recent research by Dr Moira Plant of Edinburgh, detailed in Chapter Five, suggests that the dangers of moderate drinking during pregnancy have been wildly exaggerated, but there must be several million American mothers who secretly wonder whether it was the highballs they sipped during gestation in, say, the 1950s that made their children flunk school in the seventies.

The Surgeon General's edict may have overstated the case, but it did demonstrate that the American government, unlike its British counterpart, is prepared to take positive action to limit the damage alcohol can inflict on society. And it is still the case in some circles in the US, in contrast to accepted behaviour in Europe, that pregnant women are rarely to be seen drinking even a glass of wine in public, and sudden abstention in females may be a sign of intended conception.

Alcohol has become one of the more important weapons in the lively American sex war, with women in general representing the path of moderation, just as they have since the formation of the National Women's Christian Temperance Union in 1874 in Cleveland, Ohio. One issue on which American women have taken an admirably positive stand is on drunken driving, notably through Mothers Against Drunk Driving, or MADD, an extremely powerful and well-publicized lobby.

With their national dependence on the automobile, Americans are particularly vulnerable on the drink and driving issue. Whereas stringent controls on blood-alcohol levels in drivers in Eastern Europe, where car ownership is a rare privilege, make little impact on the behaviour of society as a whole, in the US almost everyone above 16 is a frequent driver. To lose one's licence can be effectively to lose one's social life. This may be why the maximum legal blood-alcohol level for drivers is notably higher in most American states (and unspecified in some) than almost anywhere else in the world where controls on drinking and driving are imposed. Specified maximum alcohol levels in the blood can vary between 100mg/100ml and 200mg/100ml, whereas the limit in Britain and much of Europe is 80mg/100ml, and as little as 50mg/100ml in several countries.

Many responsible Americans have clearly made the only possible choice between drinking or driving in a country where the provision of public transport is so spotty. A survey published in 1987 showed dramatic reductions, by well over a third, in the proportion of drivers found to have blood-alcohol levels of both 50mg/100ml and 100mg/100ml between 1973 and 1986.

Stiffer penalties have obviously stopped many adults from drinking while driving. But since such a high proportion of accidents involve young people who have been drinking, there have been moves in many states to enforce this sensible course of action on the young by raising the minimum drinking age to 21 in all states except Wyoming, where it is 19. (The British reaction might have been to raise the minimum age for a driver's licence.)

Needless to say, researchers have been concentrating on these areas trying to assess the effects of the new limits almost before they were imposed. One report which, although funded by the official body NIAAA, or National Institute on Alcohol Abuse and Alcoholism, has not received much publicity is Asch and Levy's *The Minimum Legal Drinking Age and Traffic Fatalities*, published in 1986. The 55-page report concludes: "Our findings with respect to MLDA [minimum legal drinking age] and drinking experience are not happy ones for public officials. It does not appear that the high fatality risk presented by new drinkers can be ameliorated by raising the legal drinking age. Indeed, it is not clear that increasing the MLDA even from 18 to 21 can be expected to have a consistent effect on overall fatality rates ... The problem arises not because we permit people to drink when they are 'too young', but rather because we permit them to experience the novelty of 'new drinking' at a time when they are legally able to drive. If drinking experience preceded legal driving, a potentially important lifesaving gain might follow." In other words, the European model of introducing young people to alcohol early, gradually and non-emotively may well be the right one as far as road safety is concerned.

In any case, quite how a 20-year-old is prevented from getting a sniff of wine or whiff of beer in any circumstances is beyond the imagination of this writer. There is no doubt that in their efforts to remain within the law – and avoid horrifyingly expensive lawsuits – America's barmen are no longer simply those who serve. They must judge and take responsibility, as some well-publicized lawsuits have illustrated. It is now not unknown for a victim of a drunken driver to sue the person who served the driver with the drink that took him over the legal limit, a concept awesome in its ramifications.

Some of the results of American terror over losing a licence are good. Some areas (usually urban and sophisticated) are way ahead of their British counterparts in giving physical encouragement for drivers to abstain. Some restaurants offer unlimited free soft drinks to the designated driver, and San Francisco, for example, has a "tipsy taxi" service for those who want to drink enthusiastically.

Another major difference between American and British attitudes to alcohol can be seen at the far end of the spectrum of consumption, and in particular how those who drink too much are regarded and treated. America is the home of the enormously successful and now international organization Alcoholics Anonymous. It was started in 1935, two years after the repeal of Prohibition when America, after 13 "dry" years, suddenly and not surprisingly went very "wet" indeed. It is also hardly surprising that it promulgates the view that it is the alcoholic and not the alcohol itself that is at fault.

The AA philosophy, and indeed the philosophy of most of those treating problem drinkers in the US, is entirely medically based: that excessive drinking is a problem that can only be solved by total abstention, because there are certain people who simply cannot "handle" alcohol. By 1956, the concept of alcoholism as a disease had been fully incorporated into the legal and medical systems of the United States. This has, of course, done no harm at all in attracting funds towards treatment programmes, as well as influencing the way American society and the law regards alcoholics.

Alcohol the Disease has inevitably played its part in America's courts of law. Alcoholic veterans claim they are due the full pensions of any other military casualty, and a former presidential aide even tried using alcoholism and its effect on his memory as a defence for lying to a grand jury about his lobbying activities. It is curious to note, incidentally, that this view, that alcoholism is a disease rather than that alcohol itself is inherently dangerous or sinful, also suits the drinks industry. It certainly suits this powerful sector of the economy in the US, the world's largest importer of alcoholic drinks by far, considerably more than recent moves to put alcohol into the same category as illicit drugs. The ABC network invested six months of preparation and one of their most senior reporters, Bill Blakemore, in a television programme shown in May 1987 entitled *Alcohol and Cocaine: The Secret of Addiction*.

So rattled by this, and the mounting similar evidence of alcohol's worsening public image, is the drinks industry that it calls the high-profile members of the clearly discernible anti-alcohol industry "neo-Prohibitionists". Activists such as Michael Jacobson (ex-Nader and ex-antismoking campaigner) of the Center for Science and Public Interest [sic] have been campaigning not just for stricter laws on drink-related offences, but also for drinks labelling spelling out a warning to pregnant women, similar to health warnings on cigarette packets. A bill on this last issue in the wine state, California, was defeated in June 1987, but only by 41 votes to 29, and is still hovering in the background. Other campaigns in what appears to amount to a witch hunt against alcohol in any form concern the wildly overblown scare about traces of the carcinogen urethane sniffed out in some wines. In September 1988 the wine writer Gerald Asher pointed out in the gastronomic magazine *Gourmet* that between three and five million dollars of federal funds voted for AIDS research was to go not to the pressing practical aspects of preventing and treating this tragic scourge, but to research programmes designed to test such nebulous concepts as "the effect of alcohol use on judgment, decision making, perception of risk with respect to AIDS, and moral commitments to others".

But perhaps the most emotive issue to stir the American drinks industry in the eighties was an advertising campaign run by Seagram, the world's largest distiller and a company that controls about 20 per cent of the lucrative US hard liquor market. Seagram has been one of the few drinks companies to confront the fact that they are in business to sell a potentially harmful drug. In Britain, they ran a television campaign as early as Christmas 1986 against drunk driving, with the most subtle of corporate identities at the end. In America, they riled their competitors more dependent on sales of wine and beer than spirits with what was called their "equivalency campaign", in which they spread the message that a measure of spirits, a glass of wine and a can of beer can all contain the same amount of alcohol. Perhaps the most surprising aspect of this was that, because of the evil image of hard liquor, so few consumers were not already aware of the fact, although Seagram were accused of stacking the odds in favour of spirits by failing to spell out just how small the spirits measure had to be to have an alcohol content equivalent to that of a standard (12 US fl.oz.) can of beer.

There are obvious omissions in this briefest of voyages around the world, of which Canada is a notable one. Canada is an interesting amalgam of North American influences with more than a dollop of Mediterranean attitudes in Francophone areas such as Quebec, but with such a strong temperance movement in most of the rest of the country that Prohibition was enforced in these states during the first years of the century. When Prohibition was repealed in these states, it was generally replaced by a state monopoly in selling alcoholic drinks.

Ontario is particularly notable in any survey of the world and its drink in that it provides the setting (and some of the finance) for one of the most respected centres of research on alcohol and, in particular, alcohol control policies: the Addiction Research Foundation in Toronto.

CHAPTER ELEVEN

Alcohol as a Member of British Society

Alcohol In Britain's Social Life

Perhaps the most notable aspect of Great Britain's relationship with drink is how close it is. We share with more Mediterranean cultures such a longstanding familiarity with alcohol that, unlike Scandinavians and Americans, we rarely analyse or scrutinize it except in relation to young people and antisocial behaviour. Like some national monument, its position in our society is so entrenched that we hardly even notice it. This state of affairs may not be quite as healthy as it at first appears.

Again in stark contrast to Scandinavian and North American attitudes, teetotalism is viewed as extremely deviant behaviour in most of Britain, with the exception of odd pockets on the Celtic fringe (such as Eire, where attitudes to strong drink are much more polarized). Whereas the proportion of those who would call themselves total abstainers in the US is around 30 per cent, the comparable proportion in Great Britain was five per cent of men and 11 per cent of women in 1983, although surveys in 1987 suggest this proportion is increasing and may be nearer 16 per cent. Thanks only partly to high excise duties, we spend a greater proportion of our income, seven per cent, on alcoholic drink than any country other than Eire. The country's alcoholic drinks bill comes to more than half our annual spending on food.

Yet the actual amounts drunk by the British are but a fraction of the alcohol ingested by the average Frenchman or Italian, and are in fact less than the average per capita consumption in the US. In 1985, for example, average

French and Portuguese drank more than 13 litres of pure alcohol; Americans, Canadians, Australians and New Zealanders all drank between 7.7 and 9.2 litres; but the average British per capita consumption of pure alcohol was 7.1 litres. This is the equivalent of less than half a bottle of gin or whisky a week; or less than a bottle and a half of wine a week; or just over a pint of bitter a day. As the chart on page 144 shows, we do not rank high in the world's league table of topers.

We may not collectively drink excessively, relative to much of the rest of the world (although we drink more on average than the supposed hard-drinking Irish, Poles, Finns and Russians), but we all know individuals who consume far more than the national average and, very possibly, do so ourselves. Even at the other end of the spectrum of British alcohol consumption, stereotypically the elderly occasional sipper of sherry, stigma or self-consciousness rarely attaches itself to the act of drinking. We seem to be very, very relaxed about alcohol – unlike the prevailing British attitudes to drugs from alien cultures such as cannabis, heroin and cocaine.

Despite the fact that if used unwisely it is a potentially dangerous drug, strong drink is fully enmeshed in our society. From birth, most of us have been exposed to it in almost all aspects of play, and many aspects of work. Christenings and even births are traditionally celebrated with champagne, or at least some form of alcohol. Alcohol is an active if hardly trumpeted ingredient in gripewater and such standbys for the modern parent as Phenergan, Vallergan and even Paediatric Benylin (to a strength of about four per cent, so that a teaspoonful could easily have the same impact on an infant as a teaspoonful of gin on an adult).

Throughout childhood, most of us observe alcohol playing a central role in the social life of our parents. We see them taking a drink with friends, even our teachers, when they want to oil or cement a relationship. "Having a drink" or "going to the pub" are reinforced as legitimate and self-defining pursuits. The act of drinking is regarded as an important symbol of adulthood. Most of Britain's dominant faiths – Protestantism, Roman Catholicism, Judaism – sanction alcoholic drink by virtue of incorporating it into religious ritual. Shock and accident are widely treated with a tot of strong drink, and we have soothed our troops with (free) alcohol for centuries.

All important life events – marriage, successes at work and play – are toasted, and even funerals are marked by communal drinking. Business deals are sealed with a drink. The end of a working day or week is signalled by drinking. In many British subcultures, the pub, licensed club or, for some nowadays, the wine bar, is the social centre. For the vast majority of Britons, courtship would be unthinkable without the excuses, rituals and liberation provided by drink.

State banquets and toasts continue to play an essential symbolic part in international diplomacy. Those who govern our domestic affairs are fuelled throughout the day by bars which have never been subject to the licensing restrictions imposed outside the Palace of Westminster. A bottle of sherry, whisky or wine is seen as the all-purpose gift (although at a humbler quality level than in Japan). Drinking while driving may not be actively condoned, but the average Briton's response to this is to overcompensate once installed on a plane or train (or, indeed, anywhere with more liberal licensing laws than has been the British norm). Even many social groupings with an ostensibly sporting purpose appear to revolve around drink and drinking.

Our apparently relaxed attitude to alcohol brings a number of benefits. Because much less guilt attaches to social drinking in this country than in, say, Sweden, binge drinking is far less common (although it is notable that the more Nordic the area in Britain, the more prevalent it is: in the far northeast of Scotland, the Lutheran tradition ensures that the strong association of alcohol with guilt is sustained). We are generally much better equipped than our American counterparts to incorporate moderate drinking into our social lives. Taking just one or two drinks in a social setting, rather than consigning the evening to an inevitable six-glass path towards inebriation, is becoming ever more common. But we are still hampered by the extraordinary rituals and values we attach to all drinks that happen to contain alcohol.

It is the dogmatism with which we insist that to drink is normal, to abstain abnormal, that suggests our attitudes to alcohol are not quite as relaxed as they seem. The reason we do not take the trouble to scrutinize our drinking habits may be partly because we are reluctant about what that scrutiny may reveal. We like nothing better than to "have a drink or two" (true numeracy makes an uncomfortable drinking partner) with like-minded acquaintances, and are quite justifiably grateful for the additional allure and interest which alcohol seems to confer on them. Drinking with non-drinkers is not the same thing at all. Is this because we know they won't be wearing glasses tinted rose by ethanol when viewing us? Or because we do actually feel some guilt about our own drinking, albeit much more subtle than that experienced by our counterparts across the Atlantic and the North Sea?

Unlike members of Mediterranean cultures, the typical drinking Briton is intolerant of those who do not join him in strong drink, preferring a nonalcoholic drink instead. Social pressures to drink are still extremely strong, particularly on men. More than an element of the antipodean "drunk equals macho" phenomenon can still be observed in Britain today, especially in Scotland and parts of northern England. In many social settings in these areas, men still find it extremely difficult to be seen drinking anything other than a drink that contains alcohol. A glass of wine would be bad enough; a glass of orange juice quite unthinkable. Those who want or have to drink "soft" often have to sacrifice their social life entirely, although some more farsighted brewers are to be commended for introducing low-alcohol beers and trying to invest them with as much macho appeal as the real thing, viz. Guinness's deployment of as hard a comedian as Billy Connolly to promote a drink as soft as their low-strength lager Kaliber.

One hurdle to overcome before Britain could ever be said to have adopted sensible attitudes to drinking is the "treating" system of buying rounds of drinks at a time. Many men who pare to the minimum their contribution to the household expenses at home spend disproportionate amounts in the pub, club or bar treating fellow drinkers to drinks. It is a matter of honour in many male subcultures, typically those in which ready money is in shortest supply, that drinks be bought in rounds, which must then be returned. One of Lloyd George's many moves to limit the damage wrought by the demon drink during World War I was to introduce a "no-treating" order in 1915 outlawing this intoxicating practice. *The Spectator* at the time hailed it as a breakthrough, freeing thousands from "an expensive and senseless tyranny" (although nowadays *The Spectator* is working hard at making itself out to be the drinker's weekly, with editorials on the iniquity of random breath testing and a regular column by that most defiantly bibulous man of letters, Jeffrey Bernard). The "no-treating" order was predictably difficult to enforce and interpret – husbands were convicted for buying drinks for their wives – but some modern equivalent is surely sorely needed in areas of mass unemployment.

In the more "sophisticated" social settings of contemporary Britain, where abstention would be perfectly understandable – lunch in a West End restaurant in the middle of a heavy working day, for instance – a complicated social minuet has often to be danced between lunchers who don't want to drink, to ensure that such restraint will not upset the other lunch partner(s). Significantly, it is usually the confirmed abstainer who is least reserved about confessing his preference for a soft drink. Those who habitually indulge understand only too well the deep passions that surround the relationship between a man and his drink, one that is so rarely utterly honest. Things are slowly improving but, curiously, in much of Britain more stigma still attaches to those who choose soft drinks in company than to those who drink – even those drivers who may actually drink themselves over the legal driving limit.

The host's most serious social gaffe in contemporary Britain is to pour drinks meanly or, even worse, to run out of drink (no matter that he has laid on a wildly generous amount). Meanwhile, those who want to abstain or moderate their consumption are to be seen commuting to dinner parties with their own bottles of mineral water. There is surely something wrong with our social conditioning here. Why are we all so active in encouraging each other to drink? It may be partly a misplaced sense of generosity to provide plentiful supplies of lubrication in its most highly taxed and expensive form. But could it also be that we feel slightly guilty about our own indulgence in this drug, and feel that by spreading responsibility we are lessening our own guilt?

It does seem to me time that we took a good look at this national monument we call alcohol – not because, unlike some of those most often quoted in the media, I think we will necessarily be terrified by what we see. We might even be pleasantly surprised. But some clear-sighted, dispassionate analysis of our drinking habits should help to lessen our guilt, to heighten our sense of responsibility, to increase our enjoyment in the positive aspects of drink and to increase our respect for what is so potent a substance.

How Much and What We Drink

We hear and read a great deal about how much more we are drinking nowadays but in fact, although our per capita alcohol consumption rose rapidly throughout the sixties and most of the seventies, it had previously been at an all-time low, largely as a result of World War II and the economic vicissitudes which immediately followed it. Our average intake of beer, for example, was far higher throughout the eighteenth century and for much of the nineteenth than it is now. Likewise, our current per capita spirits consumption is a puny fraction of the amounts of gin that were downed in Gin Lane days and the brandy the Victorians soaked up. It is true, however, that the average Briton is a more enthusiastic wine drinker than he has been at any time during which records have been kept – and because wine was historically a drink mainly for the rich, it seems unlikely that Britain has ever consumed as much per head as today.

In the sixties, Britain's consumers may never have "had it so good", but they, or at least their ancestors, had certainly drunk as much. However, as our spending power has increased, we have tended to direct more and more of our disposable income towards drink, and particularly towards drinking at home. In 1986 we spent (slightly) more on alcoholic drinks than on either clothes or running our cars.

Our total drinking, calculated in per capita consumption of pure alcohol, rose steadily after World War II until the recession of 1979. It dipped in 1980, 81 and 82, since when we have been drinking very slightly more, although the 1985 figure of 7.1 litres of pure alcohol per head is still considerably below the peak of 7.5 litres we averaged in 1979. There are also healthy signs that our total national consumption is being spread over more drinking occasions: that people may be drinking more often, but drinking less when they do. Objective and statistically meaningful assessment of the nation's drinking habits is thin, but the official government surveys of 20,000 adults in 1978, 1980 and 1982 showed that the proportion of those described as heavy drinkers (more than six drinks more than once a week) was 13 per cent in 1978, 12 per cent in 1980 and only ten per cent in 1982.

The most notable recent change in our drinking habits has been not in how much we drink but in what we are drinking. Historically, we have been known as beer drinkers. Indeed, many Britons took some pride in this reputation. In 1979, however, our beer consumption peaked, with an average annual consumption of nearly 215 pints a head, representing 60 per cent of the pure alcohol the average Briton consumed. Since 1979 beer sales have fallen considerably, so that by 1985 we were drinking on average hardly more than 191 pints a year – putting us way behind, in supping order, the Germans, Czechoslovakians, Danes, Belgians, Australians and New Zealanders.

This decline in consumption of the pub's raison d'être merely mirrors the decline in the role played by the pub in British society. It probably reflects, too, the much more ingeniously innovative approach of those trying to make money from new spirit-based drinks and, more poignantly, the decreased spending power of the traditional beer drinker: the male manual worker in some of Britain's more depressed areas. The huge budgets lavished on advertising imported (or rather, apparently imported and "brewed under licence") beers have not managed to offset the slump in consumption of Britain's liquid staple, the local draught.

Our consumption of spirits also peaked in 1979, but has been creeping back after the sizable duty increases of 1981, thanks largely to the success of exotic spirit-based drinks such as Bailey's Irish Cream, Malibu, Bezique. All of these have been concocted in laboratories and polished by marketing departments, rather than emerging out of history like the spirits so much more familiar to our grandfathers. Whisky is still by far our favourite spirit and, thanks largely to the persistence of those north of the border who have an almost Nordic tradition of drinking spirits, outsells the Sassenach gin by more than three to one. And in 1987 we drank more vodka than gin for the first time ever – a new generation of consumers indeed.

But the real change in our drinking patterns is in the dramatic infiltration of wine into British society. At the end of World War II, we were hardly importing any wine at all, apart from the odd consignment from North Africa. The first of the new rash of English vineyards was planted only in the mid-fifties, so our paltry domestic supply did not exist then, either. (Even when vine growing in England was at its previous height, in the Middle Ages, we were already substantial importers of wine from Europe.) In the 1950s, wine was drunk only by those lucky enough to have access to a cellar laid down before the War. Since then, thanks to increased travel, prosperity and Europeanization, our average intake has climbed steadily, apart from a few minor hiccups – mainly the result of duty increases (demonstrating clearly how close is the relationship between price and consumption). In 1986, for example, we drank more than five times as much light table wine as in 1970: more than 11 litres a head, or 15 bottles a year.

This, of course, is much less than the hypothetical tally of a bottle and a half a week, arrived at by converting our average per capita total consumption of alcohol in any form into a wine-only form. And it is much less than – hardly an eighth of – the average per capita consumption of wine in such wine-based cultures as Portugal, France and Italy. But it demonstrates statistically what is there in every pub and licensed supermarket for all to see: that wine in Britain has exchanged its elite, almost alien aura for something very close to ubiquity. Ten years ago there were sizable tracts of the country in which the word wine had to be pronounced within audible quotation marks. Today, wine is sipped all over the country, from bottles, cartons, cardboard boxes and cans.

We are not so enthusiastic about the stronger, fortified wines such as sherry and port (and many vermouth drinkers have been lured away to more novel drinks), but Britain has another, unique type of drink to offer. "British wine" is made from reconstituted imported concentrated grape juice. It is now available at table-wine strength, but in sherry- and port-like form (the VP and QC ranges of strong, sweet liquor being two of the best known) it has represented one of the cheaper forms of alcohol.

This is the sort of drink that home wine kits result in. Like the produce of beer kits, the wide variety of liquids made by the army of home winemakers endemic in any country with such relatively high duties on drink is often ignored in official estimates of our alcohol intake. (Domestic distillation is, unlike in Ireland, Scotland, the USA, the USSR and Poland, virtually unknown in England.) In 1983, Britain's home brewers and winemakers turned out a minimum of an additional 360 million pints of beer and 320,000 bottles of wine. This level of domestic enterprise boosts our average alcohol consumption to such a level that it accounts for about six per cent of all the energy we derive from food.

Many observers – and, not surprisingly, the wine trade – feel that our move towards wine drinking is a good thing, that it signifies a certain maturity in our attitude to alcohol. Wine is, after all, a generally much more expensive way to consume alcohol than beer or spirits. What researchers call a "unit" of alcohol – an eighth of a bottle of most basic wines, a half pint of bitter or a single measure of spirits – cost in a pub about £1, 50p and 70p respectively in 1987. An affection for wine therefore suggests something rather less suspect than a headlong rush to inebriation. And through wine, we are acquiring the healthy Continental habit of ingesting our alcohol with food, thus moderating its ravages on the body.

Our new love affair with wine is just one example of the overall direction of Britain's drinking habits, away from drinks with a high alcohol content. In drawing rooms all over England, gins and tonics and whiskies and sodas are giving way to glasses of wine and even mineral water. The corkscrew has taken over from the ice bucket; the cocktail cabinet has joined the Wurlitzer as a curious artefact from the recent past. Tougher drink-driving laws have had very obvious effects on digestif drinking, and the restaurant trollies loaded with brandies and liqueurs clink increasingly pointlessly between the tables.

Meanwhile, Britain has solemnly been shipping oceans of French water, in bottles, across the Channel, while gulping our own Highland Spring, Malvern and Ashbourne with almost as much enthusiasm, to satisfy a thirst most of us never knew we had before the early 1970s. More recently, low-alcohol beers, wines and wine coolers have managed to find enthusiasts, although the British duty system ludicrously has until recently penalized those who drink wine coolers, charging full table-wine duty on any wine-based drink containing more than 1.2 per cent alcohol (2 per cent is the cut-off point for shandies and the like).

Such is the duty on spirits, however, that they are actually quite cheap in Britain today, certainly relative to prices in most of the rest of Europe. Scotch whisky is one of our more noticeable exports; after France, we are the world's biggest exporters of alcoholic drinks, most of them spirits. This doubtless helps the leverage the spirits industry is able to bring to bear on government, but does little to encourage the nation's quite commendable tendency to take its alcohol in more dilute forms.

Regional Variation In Drinking Habits

The cliché is that the Scots and the Irish are drunks, on a heady mix of beer and Scotch or stout and Irish whiskey respectively; that the Welsh are kept sober most of the time by the chapel and their womenfolk; and that in England, northerners drink more, mainly in the form of beer, than those in the south. Like most clichés, it is inaccurate. One has only to go in search of a pub in some of the towns of the far north of Scotland or to a rugby match at Cardiff Arms Park to get some inkling of this.

As already outlined, our drinking habits have been changing, which means that most available statistics on who drinks what where (which tend to be a bit harder to come by than those on how much we collectively drink) lag behind the reality. The effects of increasing health awareness, for example, in some sectors of the community (usually those who can afford this luxury) on lowering the average alcohol content of what they drink is not fully reflected, just as the available statistics probably suggest that Britain's more economically deprived areas have slightly more money to spend on drink than they do, in fact, today.

There is also a geographical drinking phenomenon that is subjectively observable but seems never to have been objectively quantified: that in general those country dwellers who do drink tend to drink more than their urban counterparts. Perhaps this is a legacy from the days when a rural life involved considerably more physical activity than today's clamber in and out of the Range Rover. It may seem paradoxical that those who presumably have farthest to drive and least recourse to public transport ingest the most alcohol, but then country roads are presumably much more difficult to police – and, the country drinkers may argue, less populated and therefore less hazardous than busy urban thoroughfares.

It is observably true, too, that it is in the country's most "sophisticated" areas such as inner London, Bath, and the more salubrious quarters of Edinburgh and Glasgow, all of them urban, that low-alcohol or no-alcohol drinks such as mineral water have infiltrated what was the drinking community most effectively – to the horror of restaurateurs who have been used to bolstering their income with the much higher mark-ups they can levy on wine. The alcohol-free business lunch, an almost unknown phenomenon ten years ago, may be good for the liver and soul but strikes fear in the heart of many caterers.

The most recent analysis of household expenditure on drink, carried out in 1986, showed that most money was directed towards alcohol in Greater London (£9.27 per household per week), and least in temperate Northern Ireland, where a third of the men and a half of the women are teetotal (£5.30 against a national average of £8.42, out of a total weekly overall family spend of £185.02). These are clear regional variations quite independent of the demographics of the region, total expenditure and income.

Mintel's most recent report, *Changing Lifestyles in the Alcoholic Drinks Market*, contains probably the most up-to-date outline of our drinking habits available. It was published in December 1987 and was specifically designed to show the recent impact of sophisticated marketing and health concerns. Mintel found that the Scots in general are the most sober regional subgroup in mainland Britain, 22 per cent of them claiming to be total abstainers. London and the south, and Wales harbour the highest proportions of those who claimed to drink every day: 12 and 11 per cent respectively, according to this survey which relies on self-reporting – almost certainly the least reliable method of analysing drinking habits. It has been firmly established, for example, that the interview technique of gathering information on drinking habits never accounts for more than 60 per cent of the alcohol shown by Customs and Excise statistics to have been sold, and that people admit to drinking considerably more if they are either questioned by a computer or never forced to tick the highest consumption category in a questionnaire.

It is clear, however, that there are quite definite regional differences in drinking patterns. The Scots tend to be binge drinkers, Mintel finding far fewer respondents in Scotland, for instance, admitting to drinking "most days", compared with elsewhere. The Welsh, meanwhile, had the lowest proportion of total abstainers – and the Welsh, and drinkers in the west of England, are the nation's most enthusiastic habitués of pubs and clubs. So much for stereotypes.

There is one apparent marked difference between the Scots and those south of the border. According to official health records, the Scots are statistically more likely to die from acute liver disease or cirrhosis. This suggests such a marked, consistent and medically inexplicable contrast between the supposed health of livers in, say, Dumfries and Carlisle that it seems likely, as one researcher demonstrates, that there is simply a discrepancy in recording procedures north and south of the border. It is certainly true that many English doctors have been loth to spell out the incriminating word c-i-r-r-h-o-s-i-s on a death certificate, because in England until July 1984 all alcohol-related deaths had to be reported to the coroner. It has been suggested that this tact underestimates total deaths from cirrhosis by 80 per cent, although more recently qualified doctors are trained to overcome their squeamishness on this issue and to keep more comprehensive and more honest records.

As detailed in Chapter Five, alcohol is not the only cause of liver damage, and the high mortality rate in Scotland may well be caused by Scottish dietary or social habits quite unconnected with the distilleries or Scottish & Newcastle Breweries. It is conventionally thought that little-and-often drinkers, such as the wine drinkers of France, are those most at risk from cirrhosis. But in France, the one region with a notably high cirrhosis mortality rate is the northwest, land of the apple (and cow) rather than the grape. And there is the tendency of the supposedly cirrhotic Scots to be "binge" drinkers. More research is clearly needed.

The rate of convictions for drunkenness has traditionally been slightly higher in Scotland than in England and Wales, possibly because of differing legal practices rather than a geographical variation in raucousness. But the rate has declined rapidly in Scotland, not so much in England and Wales, since 1975 – partly because of new and apparently enlightened ways of rehabilitating drunkenness offenders north of the border, and possibly partly as a result of the licensing laws being relaxed there in 1976.

There is also some evidence to suggest that drunken drivers in Scotland tend to be more drunken than their counterparts south of the border. Overall, however, in line with Edinburgh's status as Paris of the North and Glasgow's newfound glory as European City of Culture, Scotland's drinking habits seem relatively civilized. This may have something to do with the fact that Scotland is the site of such important research on alcohol use and misuse as Britain can muster, as well as the establishment of detoxification centres as successful as Albyn House in Aberdeen, which may now fairly be regarded as Britain's capital of human detoxification as well as decompression.

Those who get into the grimy and depressing area of statistics on hospital admissions concerned with alcohol abuse find some wide regional variations, but research has shown that these are largely due to different medical provisions, capacities and capabilities. For a long time, for example, it was thought that the incidence of drunkenness so bad as to require hospitalization was 12 times higher in the Highlands than in Kent – until it was realised that it is rather easier to be treated as an outpatient in densely populated Kent than in the Grampians.

Drink and the Sexes – the Bare Bones

The flesh of how alcohol affects the different sexes is there for all brave women to see in Chapter Five, but the statistics on how much women actually drink in comparison with men do reflect the fact that in this sense, at least, we are very definitely – and very unfairly, in my view – the weaker sex.

In Britain, as all over the rest of the world, men drink far more than women. According to recent British surveys, men drink on average nearly three times as much as women: just under 20 units and seven units a week respectively. One 1982 survey of 20,000 adults indicated that 21 per cent of men admitted to being heavy drinkers (more than once a week and more than six drinks on each occasion) whereas only one per cent of women did. At the other end of the scale, twice as many women as men described themselves as abstainers.

The picture has been changing rapidly, however. By the time Mintel conducted a survey just two years later, admittedly on a much smaller scale, more than half as many women as men – eight per cent as opposed to 15 per cent – said they drank "most days". Those who deal with alcohol problems report a substantial increase in the number of women seeking help – although it may be partly because there is so much more stigma attached to the female alcohol abuser that women seek help earlier. In 1964, one in five members of Alcoholics Anonymous was female. Now one in three members of this extremely social group is a woman. Although the Merseyside, Cheshire and Lancashire Council on Alcoholism report that they have as many women as men among their clients under 30, a recent analysis of drinking trends suggests that the current rate of increase of alcohol problems in women is no greater than that in men. Interestingly, only about ten per cent of convicted drunken drivers are women, despite the growing number who now drive menfolk who have lost their licences.

In one curious and worrying respect, British women seem to differ markedly from the women of other nationalities. In most countries, even such varied and emancipated countries as the USA, France and the Netherlands, the female cirrhosis mortality rate is half or considerably less than that of the males of the population. In Britain, however, according to World Health Organization statistics, women are very nearly as likely to die of cirrhosis as men. One wonders whether this anomaly is due to some quirk of medical reporting, which seems unlikely, or reflects the ravages of overenthusiastic consumption on the delicate female constitution – but why in Britain in particular? Comparative statistics on this fascinating aspect of the world's drinking habits are not as reliable as most, but suggest, in fact, that British women drink rather less of the national total than women in other countries – about 25 per cent (less than our French or American sisters).

Certainly in less privileged households in which alcohol is consumed heavily, it will be the woman who always feeds herself last, thereby giving herself the least nutritional defence, an important factor, against the ill-effects of alcohol. Women are also more likely to choose drinks such as cocktails or exotic new branded products whose strength is much less obvious or easy to calculate than the standard measures of beer, whisky or gin.

Those women whose drinking reaches harmful levels give quite different reasons for drinking than men, more usually citing drink as a release from strains, domestic strife or role conflicts than the social benefits and camaraderie (a.k.a. the pub) often cited by men. One researcher has suggested that the reason so many more women take antidepressants than men is that they rarely have access to what he calls "the therapy of the pub", whereby a man can relieve himself of stress and strain by ritualized argument in a non-domestic atmosphere associated with "play", i.e. discuss sport and politics at the bar.

Perhaps the most worrying finding in Mintel's 1987 report concerned their analysis of attitudes to alcohol and health among moderate drinkers. While a significant 64 per cent of men said they did not think that alcohol affected health, the proportion of the more vulnerable sex who agreed with them was even higher: 70 per cent. Have they not been reading the papers?

Drink and Age, and Spare Cash

Many of us know from very personal experience that there are marked differences in the amounts we drink at different stages in our lives.

Most of us remember feeling we could drink almost limitless quantities in our early twenties, whether through youthful vigour or relative freedom from responsibilities at home and work. Consumption drops sharply among 25-34 year olds, who are presumably most stretched financially and confined physically while bringing up young families, only to rise gradually in the next two decades as we have fewer demands on our income and fewer reasons to wake up early and clear-headed in the morning. Mintel's report found the greatest frequency of drinking in the 55+ age group, who drank more than three times as often as 15-25 year olds. The much more objective 1980 survey of population trends confirms the picture, finding in the over-65 group, as well as the highest proportion of total abstainers, some extremely heavy drinkers, a finding which many lay observers would confirm. One recent Scottish study found that men drank 56 per cent more once they retired.

It seems to me that alcohol can play an extremely useful role in old age. As long as it does not tempt the elderly to venture out or drive in an intoxicated state, and is not taken in such quantities or circumstances that it seriously prejudices nutrition or increases the risk of shattering brittle bones, it is surely a most desirable mellower of the autumn of life. I cannot imagine worrying unduly about increasing my risk of liver cirrhosis by what I drink in my seventies, should I live to enjoy the wine I am now laying down for well into the next century – although I know that society in general worries about old ladies "who drink".

Drinking habits at the other end of the age range are an even more emotive issue. There is evidence that alcohol abuse is now a problem among some very young Britons. The rate of convictions for drunkenness among teenagers has risen quite exceptionally over the past two decades, perhaps partly because police have been encouraged to take a firmer line with soccer hooligans. And the proportion of teenagers among those prosecuted for drunken driving has long been high, an appropriate term. The driving problem is a specific one of learning to cope with two fairly novel activities concurrently. If the adult population was more adult and censorious in its attitude to drinking and driving, the teenage problem might well be considerably less severe.

In this country we are relatively liberal about introducing children to alcohol – perhaps slightly less so than in Mediterranean countries such as France, where many children are introduced to wine at a very young age (and may legally be served at 14), but certainly much more so than in Scandinavia and America where the minimum legal drinking age in almost all states is 21, unthinkably high to most of Britain's teenagers.

Because the majority of children in Britain encounter their first drink in the home, it is important for their future attitudes that drinking is viewed sensibly and responsibly by the adults in that home. This is particularly true since there is little convincing evidence that alcohol educational programmes targeted at young people actually work (unlike similar campaigns warning of the dangers of smoking). The Brewers' Society have thoughtfully given substantial funding to a project on assessing the value of alcohol education in schools.

A detailed study of 13 to 16 year olds undertaken in 1976 showed not only that parental attitudes to alcohol have a real effect on those of teenagers, but also that in this age bracket there was no difference in drinking habits between girls and boys. All the signs are that the female adults of tomorrow will be drinking more and more. This is why it is important to disseminate the unpalatable facts about how poorly the female body withstands the predations of alcohol.

As in so many facets of contemporary Britain, there are signs of polarization of attitudes to drinking among young people. Some do genuinely seem to have a much more mature view of drink, and a more responsible way of handling it, than their (often middle-class) parents. Even if this is motivated by the fact that teenagers find it more difficult to pay fines for drunken driving than their parents, it still bodes well for the future. Others, more often working class and possibly even recent or concurrent solvent abusers, have been seen to seize on alcohol, as on a wide range of other drugs, as a ubiquitous means of escape from grim reality in a depressed urban landscape.

Religious and Ethnic Groups

It illustrates well how important alcohol is to man that most religions have a clearly discernible relationship with it, not to say policy on it. Muslims abjure it; Methodists and fundamentalist Protestants abhor it; the Church of England condones it; among Roman Catholics, even many clerics seem to revel in it. Two groups have long fascinated alcohol researchers on both sides of the Atlantic: the Irish and Jewish communities. Indeed, much of the American research is founded on study of those groups which have somehow, in modern America, escaped alcohol problems. This has concentrated attention on the temperate Chinese, and the Jewish community which has, until recently increased assimilation, had a much lower incidence of alcohol problems than the rest of the population, in marked contrast to the Irish.

Some possible reasons for this contrast are immediately apparent. Whereas the typical Irish community is made up of total abstainers and extremely heavy drinkers, who are usually male and drink together outside the home, alcohol in the form of kosher wine is consumed in many Jewish households every Friday night as part of the Kiddush ritual involving the whole family. Jewish children therefore learn about drink and moderate drinking from their parents, and alcohol is not invested with what might be called forbidden-fruit value – a lesson which many think could well be applied widely outside Jewish communities. Drunkenness is accepted as a fact of Irish life, but is gently ridiculed by Jews. This view may well have been encouraged in the past by the mores of a ghetto community keen not to draw attention to itself.

Research comparing alcohol consumption and problems in Manchester and parts of India has shown that even Muslims can become dependent on alcohol when taken out of a traditional Muslim environment: one survey put the proportion of alcoholics among Muslims resident in Greater Manchester at three per cent, whereas even social drinking is rare among Muslims resident in India. There are also signs that young Asian women resident in Britain by no means automatically abstain.

Alcohol and Occupation, or Are Doctors Really Drunks?

Many of us feel we hardly need expensive research to confirm a strong correlation between alcohol consumption and occupation. Advertising folk, caterers, entertainers, journalists, medicos, publishers, sailors and, of course, members of the drinks trade itself spring to mind as providing some of the more striking examples of professionally enthusiastic consumption (what chance the liver of a wine journalist married to a restaurateur?).

Some jobs incorporate alcohol in the working routine. Those in and around the drinks trade, from publican to gin salesman, bonded warehousekeeper, wine merchant, distillery worker, even exciseman, all have obvious and constant exposure to strong drink during the working day. But in many less obvious workplaces, the key to the office drinks cabinet is seen as one of the tokens of professional advancement – together with the sanctioning of lunchtime drinking on an expense account. Alcohol is used as a positive reward for employees above a certain level by many employers, who rarely seem to examine the consequences of unrestrained consumption during the working day.

Employers are gradually being schooled in this respect. Indeed, the employer's role as monitor of alcohol problems is becoming a key factor in the theory of good management – even the police have a special unit to deal with this problem in the force. But it seems as though most employers still, in practice, accept drinking in their employees within surprisingly narrow limits: too little can jeopardize the business of socializing with clients (and colleagues); too much may lead to summary dismissal, as though the problem were entirely independent of the employer and the structure of the job.

Of course, there is one demanding and underresearched occupation which in many cases exposes the worker to drink throughout the working routine without supervision of any sort: that of housewife or "homemaker". Young children may not supervise, but they do monitor, which can act as a natural brake on the daytime drinking habits of the parent. But the reaction of many who are suddenly left alone in the home all day with unaccustomed free time, whether because of the departure of offspring or bereavement, is to turn too enthusiastically to the bottle.

Martin Plant, Director of the University of Edinburgh's Alcohol Research Group, has conducted some of the most illuminating research on the links between occupation and drinking habits, devoting a whole book to it in 1979. In *Drinking Careers*, he showed how heavy drinkers tended to gravitate towards those professions in which free or subsidized drink was most available. This, again, is a phenomenon with which many of us are familiar. He also showed, however, how some of the heaviest drinkers deliberately left the drinks trade (he studied Edinburgh distillery and brewery workers in particular) in order to cut down their drinking, and managed to continue to keep their consumption down.

Dr Plant also isolated those factors in a job that were most likely to encourage consumption and, possibly, lead to alcohol problems. Availability is, of course, of prime importance and affects the drinking habits of many executives and those in the catering and drinks trades. Company directors as a group, according to Plant, have "very funny liver function tests", with a likelihood of some damage in one in every eight cases according to one study. Even when no alcohol is available on the premises, social pressures to go drinking with co-workers can be a major factor, as anyone who has spent Friday evening in a pub can testify.

Those who are self-employed or work unsupervised are also more prey to the ravages of overindulgence, but a particular pressure felt by, for example, travelling salesmen and sailors is being separated from normal social and sexual routines and relationships – in other words, not being supervised by family or friends. It is also observable, apparently, that alcohol problems tend to develop in those with either a particularly high income and plenty of money to lavish on the drinks cabinet, or a particularly low one with many a sorrow to drown. Collusion and conspiracy might also be cited, in that certain professions tend to drink heavily and encourage those in it to drink. The

CIRRHOSIS MORTALITY RATE IN VARIOUS OCCUPATIONS

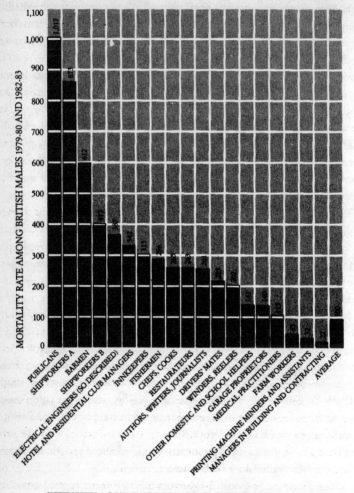

MORTALITY RATE AMONG BRITISH MALES 1979-80 AND 1982-83

SHIPWORKERS A: DECK, ENGINE-ROOM HANDS, BARGEMEN, LIGHTERMEN, BOATMEN
SHIPWORKERS B: DECK, ENGINEERING AND RADIO OFFICERS, PILOTS

No comparable figures for women are available from these surveys as the numbers involved
were too small.

drinks trade is an obvious example, but Dr Plant, interestingly (or challengingly?), cited doctors as well in this 1979 study.

Stressful, hazardous occupations may also encourage (and perhaps excuse) heavy drinking. This has been the traditional excuse for the medical profession's hard-drinking record. In the 1970s doctors were more than three times as likely to die from chronic liver disease or cirrhosis than the average, the standardized mortality ratio for the population as a whole being 100. This poor example has hindered the cause of those who would like to see general practitioners taking a much more active role in alcohol education and monitoring problem drinking. It must also be said that within the medical profession there is wide disparity between the most vocal elements on alcohol as a problem, and the everyday practitioner who was doubtless as horrified as the rest of the British drinking public when the Royal Colleges suddenly halved their recommended safe limits of consumption, to 24 grams a day for men and 16 grams a day for women, in 1987.

The media psychiatrist Professor Anthony Clare has been one member of the medical profession most publicly to berate drinking practice among fellow doctors. He suggests, for example, that bars in medically responsible organizations, such as hospitals and the Royal Colleges, which have issued such stern guidelines to the rest of us, should not serve alcoholic drinks at lunchtime.

The bibulous doctor is an easy target, and one that the Junior Health Minister, Edwina Currie, could not resist at Alcohol Concern's conference in the autumn of 1987. But the Minister was rather out of date. Doctors seem to have tightened up their drinking considerably since seeing how prominently they figured in Martin Plant's league table, published in 1979 but referring to mortality as far back as 1970-72. By 1983, doctors were only 1.15 times more likely to die from cirrhosis as the average member of the population. This may be because of the much higher proportion of women doctors a decade later, or because training on alcohol problems in the medical profession is now much more concentrated and deliberate.

This new restraint shown by doctors has to be seen in the light of the fact that the cirrhosis and chronic liver disease mortality rate of the population as a whole rose by about a third between 1970 and 1982, from around 1,500 to just over 2,000 deaths a year in England and Wales. This not only suggests that in absolute terms doctors are drinking half, and not a third, as much as they were in the early seventies, but also puts into perspective how small a base was used for these figures.

Whatever the basis of this now somewhat dated research, however (the arbitrary-seeming categories were determined by the Office of Population Censuses and Surveys), the incidence of liver cirrhosis in pub workers and those who go to sea for a living is frightening. One can only hope that all those who dream of a pub in the country are aware that publicans are more than ten times more likely than the population as a whole to die of cirrhosis: further evidence for the theory that it is the regular drinker who is most likely to develop liver damage (company directors, for example, and the French as a whole), rather than the "binge" drinker whose problems are more likely to be social (manual workers and the Finns). Liver function tests, incidentally, are notoriously inexact, but the French set such store by them that some employers insist that prospective employees are tested.

Attitudes to Drink

Because of the paucity of objective data, the author brazenly adopts an entirely subjective approach at this point. In contemporary British society, no one wins points for being a fanatical teetotaller. Those who have decided that the path of abstention is the only possible one for them (sometimes because they have experienced problems in controlling their alcohol consumption) can find life extremely tedious as they face inquisitions and hectoring from the drinking majority.

We British do not take kindly to those who refuse our most treasured symbol of friendship, the offer of an alcoholic drink. Monetary value has nothing to do with it. We take it as a rejection whether our offer of a drink is interpreted as an ultra-economical glass of tapwater or a wildly overpriced nonalcoholic cocktail. The important bonding process is that we are prepared to indulge in a recreational drug together, thereby lowering our defences and loosening our inhibitions.

Each sort of drinking and drink has its own image. Beer drinking is viewed as a worthy, serious, almost radical activity if it involves seeking out small-batch brews from breweries other than the giants who dominate the drinks industry. When the beer comes out of a mass-market ringtop can, however, straight into a swaying young gullet, then beer drinking is associated with football hooliganism and other examples of the yob behaviour that is so nationally mortifying.

Wine drinking has lost a great deal of its elitist mystique, but those who talk about it are generally held to be pontificating or showing off rather than conversing. Wine as an apéritif has a perceptibly female image, and it is a brave

man who orders a glass of Liebfraumilch in a Toxteth or Tyneside pub –
although in the less beleaguered southeast, drinking wine, and champagne in
particular, is associated with sophistication whichever the sex of the drinker.
Wine is also seen, usually but not always quite rightly, as the most civilized
form of alcohol, a drink that encourages contemplative sipping, often at the
table, rather than thoughtless toping.

One could be forgiven for feeling that spirits retain their glamorous
aura of, essentially male, prosperity chiefly thanks to television drama. Directors on both sides of the Atlantic have latched gratefully on to the convention
of pouring, sipping and clinking of ice cubes as a way of injecting action into
a set piece of dialogue in opulent settings from Dallas to the BBC's drawing
rooms down Howards' Way. In real life, the traditional spirits are seen as
drinks for traditional people, set in their ways and the rituals they have
evolved for communion with their favoured distillate. ("Just two drops of
angostura"; "now exactly half as much Malvern water", etc.)

Newer spirits or, more usually, spirit-based drinks cultivate an image
of unabashed trendiness, of frenetically youthful gyration and courting ritual
almost concurrent with gulping the likes of Malibu, Bezique, Bacardi and
Pernod. That cunning advertising can entirely recreate the image of a drink
has been proven most successfully with Pernod, the only one of those named
whose strength is on a par with full-strength spirits such as gin and whisky.
(It is surely either shocking or absurd that there is most room for confusion
as to alcoholic strength with those drinks most likely to be drunk by those
who are most inexperienced at both drinking and driving.) In France, diluted
pastis is the ubiquitous and somewhat démodé slurp of the peasant farmer and
urban lower classes. In this country, thanks to heavy marketing and disco
promotion, with boring old water is only the fourth most common way of
drinking Pernod: lemonade, blackcurrant and orange juice are all more
popular mixers. No wonder the French think we're barbarians.

Attitudes to drunkenness are, not surprisingly, more variable. Gentle
inebriation is a majority state in British adults at certain times of the week,
Friday and Saturday nights in particular, which is why it is difficult for us to
be anything other than tolerant towards it. We tend to admire those who can
"hold their drink", this being commonly associated with good breeding. At
the office party, for example, the gentlemen are expected to keep a straight
back, whereas the sales clerks may indulge in a bit of horseplay – even if each
group has consumed exactly the same amount of alcohol. We tend to behave
under the influence of alcohol as we have been conditioned to.

We are generally indifferent to how much someone may consume, and object only if their resulting actions embarrass us. Particularly if we are drinking, too, we do not like to be reminded that drinking can have unpleasant side-effects. We tend to stick to those who appear to drink at our own rate. The average Briton does not remark on his inebriation, and prefers those who do not too forcibly remind him of it by becoming drunk much faster or more slowly.

On the One Hand ... Big Business and Government

Much more than in the wine-producing countries of Europe, the power within the drinks trade in Britain is concentrated in remarkably few hands, and is becoming even more concentrated as the takeover tide washes over the drinks companies. Between 1960 and 1980 the number of commercial brewers, those who produce what is still our favourite form of alcohol, fell from 247 to 81, reflecting a shrinkage in choice for the British beer drinker over the sixties and seventies greater than in any country other than Sweden and the US. Yet even by 1980, of those 81 brewers only seven were producing 70 per cent of all the beer drunk in Britain.

The big brewers also have an interest in about 80 per cent of all pubs, and control or are sister companies to most of the big off-licence chains: Victoria Wine/Haddows, Peter Dominic/Bottoms Up, Roberts/Arthur Cooper, Thresher/Ashe & Nephew, Augustus Barnett/Galleon, Peatling & Cawdron and others. Most of them run large wine and spirit wholesaling companies in tandem, supplying not only their own outlets but the catering trade and many of the cash-and-carry outlets and the supermarkets, which now represent the only major (and extremely vigorous) competition for the brewers in the retail distribution of alcoholic drinks.

In production rather than distribution, power is even more concentrated, not only in beer but also in spirits (England's wine industry is so small as to be negligible in big-business terms). Only two out of the 114 Scotch whisky distilleries, Macallan and Glenfarclas, are run absolutely independently of either any other distillery or any other drinks company. The industry giant, the apparently somewhat effete Distillers Company, controlled 38 distilleries (and a heady blend of English spirits including Gordon's, Booth's and Tanqueray gin), and had for many years been engaged in fierce competition with what was regarded as the strongest independent Scotch whisky group, Bell's. By 1987, Distillers and Bell's found themselves sister companies and, what's more, owned by a brewer, Guinness.

An American, Swiss-based, survey of international corporations with interests in alcoholic drinks undertaken in 1980 (*Alcoholic Beverages – Dimensions of Corporate Power*, by John Cavanagh and Frederick F. Clairmonte) showed that four out of the seven leading transnational corporations involved in alcoholic drinks were British. The Imperial Group (Courage, Saccone & Speed, Roberts & Cooper, etc.); Grand Metropolitan (Watneys, International Distillers & Vintners, Gilbey Vintners, Morgan Furze, Peter Dominic, Croft, etc.); Lonrho (Ashe & Nephew and bottling companies, since sold to Whitbread, Eschenauer); and Allied-Lyons (Allied Breweries, Grants of St James's, Hatch Mansfield, Victoria Wine, Harveys of Bristol, Cockburn, etc.) each had total sales of more than five billion US dollars, together with Philip Morris, the South African Rembrandt Group and Coca-Cola.

Of course, since 1980 there have been some major rearrangements in the wake of the takeover fever that hit the financial world in the mid-1980s, not least the result of what might be called the advent of the Australians, but they have all resulted in yet further concentration of power. By the end of 1987, Allied-Lyons and Whitbread shared a wine and spirit wholesaling operation, and since Hanson acquired Imperial, considerable wine and spirit interests have been sold on from Imperial to Grand Met. The major independent London distiller James Burroughs has been swallowed up into Whitbread. And so it goes on.

Even though the drinks industry is run by relatively few individuals, individuals who tend to be both conservative and Conservative, it is relatively important to the British economy. About 100,000 people are employed directly producing and handling drink, but far more than that work in the UK's 80,000 pubs, 35,000 clubs, 48,000 off-licences and other places that trade in drink. The proportion of the British workforce engaged in or around the drinks industry may be low compared with the French figure of more than ten per cent, but it is still high enough (some generous estimates put it at 750,000) to count in Whitehall when increases in duty are being considered.

We are, furthermore, the world's third biggest importers of alcoholic drink after the US and West Germany, shipping in more than a billion US dollars' worth, mainly wine and brandy, to keep us afloat. But what gives the drinks industry great power within government circles is its export performance. After France, we are the world's most important exporter of drink, notably Scotch whisky which is still Scotland's number one export (if the imported element in Scotland's burgeoning computer industry is taken out of its export value) and Britain's fifth. In 1986 Scotch whisky exports topped

£1 billion, but we also export gin, some wine and beer and a lot of licences to brew and distil.

The Scotch Whisky Association and the Brewers' Society are prosperous and powerful trade associations occupying prime London West End sites (the SWA's a mere pied-à-terre compared with their handsome headquarters in Edinburgh). It says something about the fragmented, competitive nature and relative unprofitability of the wine trade in Britain that the Wine & Spirit Association, with its demanding work decoding the complexities of the wine laws of Brussels, is crammed into a few tiny rooms on the second floor of a building in the City of London belonging to the Vintners' Company, founded several centuries before its distilling equivalent. Curiously, there is no single body designed to represent the combined interests of the drinks industry, which may explain why there has been so little apparent response to the attack mounted by the bodies outlined in the next section.

Since beer is the national drink, on many counts the most generously funded trade body is the Brewers' Society. It has funded several research projects on alcohol as well as being the most useful statistical source. The Scotch Whisky Association has consistently allocated funds to worthy research projects and has contributed substantially to the support of the Alcohol Research Group in Edinburgh.

Apart from these donations, which the real cynic might well think constitute more window dressing than genuine concern, the drinks trade has so far done too little to show the general public that it is confronting the darker side of the chemical that is common to all its products. There have been leaflets, the occasional educational programme aimed at young drinkers, grants towards helping alcoholics and educating the medical profession, but there has been little convincing public answer to the anti-alcohol onslaught so apparent in the media in the last year or two. One heartening recent initiative, however, has been the Brewers' Society's "Wheelwatch" and "Agewatch" schemes to counter, respectively, drunken driving and underage drinking.

It is hardly, as shown in Chapter Two, that there is no case to make for the virtues of moderate drinking. Alcohol study specialist Richard Grindal of the Scotch Whisky Association did make many of the relevant points in a series of articles in the publican's newspaper, *The Morning Advertiser*, but was not exactly making new converts there. Knowing many of the parties involved, I suspect that the apparent public silence of the drinks trade has been because of the lack of coordination between the various parties and the philosophical differences among them.

The wine-importing faction want to argue that their form of alcohol is less socially dangerous than beer and spirits. The distilling contingent might want to expound the message of Seagram's "equivalency campaign", so deeply unpopular with the American wine trade because it spelt out the equivalency of units of alcohol in different forms. The brewers might well demand of the wine brigade more time and money than they were able to spare, and a less punitive relative duty structure. And so the drinking public has been left with the impression that the drinks trade could muster no rebuttal of the much-publicized attacks on alcohol.

Indeed, so ignorant does the drinks trade keep its customers of alcohol as an issue, that it has been extremely reluctant even to impart the most useful information of all: the alcoholic content of each drink. It has taken years even to ensure that all labellers use the same scale of measure of alcoholic strength: percentage by volume. No wonder those brought up on proof spirit are confused. Only from May 1988 must all alcoholic drinks, by law, state their alcoholic strength in percentage by volume on the label. The brewers' system of using specific gravity rather than the percentage alcohol which replaces it served only to confuse.

In a consumer survey conducted in 1986 (*Tomorrow's Generation of New Brands – the Light and Low Phenomenon*, by Adsearch of London), drinkers were asked to guess the strength of lager, table wine and wine coolers. They were given a major clue by being told that water was 0 per cent and standard spirits 40 per cent. Even so, they thought lager was nearly seven times stronger than it really is (about 3.5 per cent), that wine was nearly 22 per cent when in fact it averages about 11, and that coolers were also more than twice as strong as they really are.

Somehow, the drinks trade's coyness about Alcohol, the Chemical, is symptomatic of its attitude to Alcohol, the Problem. *Harpers Wine and Spirit Gazette*, the wine trade's weekly magazine, broke its silence on the subject by publishing an editorial in late 1986 calling for a trade policy on alcohol. The response was merely a letter from one of the trade's most eminent gentlemen, suggesting that the problem didn't really exist because some of us, notably us in the wine trade, could cope much better with a given amount of alcohol than others.

In April 1987, the *Off-Licence News* devoted three of its tabloid pages to a paper delivered by an advertising man at its annual seminar, headlined: "Prepare to fight the 'growing threat' from anti-alcohol set". The adman, not surprisingly, suggested they did a bit of generic advertising.

By September 1987, *Harpers'* editorial started: "There is little doubt that the single most threatening aspect to the trade in the short, medium and long-term outlook is the growing voice of the anti-alcohol campaign. For too long in the past the trade has shied away from answering criticism and from defending itself against irresponsible and unjustified attacks. However [the] director of the Wine & Spirit Association ... was able to state that the trade, in fact, had now begun to get its act together." Performances of this act have so far been notably low-key.

Inertia and infighting are but two of three possible reasons why the drinks trade has been so slow to adopt a policy on what they call "the social aspects of alcohol". Until those outlined in the following section became more strident, they didn't have to. The drinks trade and government have been happy partners in the business of making money from selling alcohol ever since 1643, when Cromwell's Parliament first imposed a levy on beer. And the relationship between the drinks trade and the present Conservative Government is a particularly close one. The Conservative Party has consistently received some of its biggest donations from Allied-Lyons, and in 1987 60 MPS had a direct financial interest in the drinks trade, David Mitchell, Minister of State at the Department of Transport, no less, owing his means to the Fleet Street watering hole El Vino.

In 1986, for example, excise duty on alcoholic drinks provided the Exchequer with more than £4 billion, or nearly four per cent of its revenue. Indeed, so cosy has been the agreement between the drinks trade and the Government that Alcohol, the Problem, should be ignored so as not to jeopardize Alcohol, the Moneyspinner, that the report of the "Think Tank" in 1979 on Alcohol Policies was given an extremely frosty reception.

The Central Policy Review Staff's conclusions in *Alcohol Policies* were: "The trends in misuse justify Government concern. Without Government initiatives and a better concerted set of policies these trends are likely to continue. The effectiveness of action depends critically on public attitudes. Impinging on these will require not only patience and caution but also sustained effort. The institutional arrangements need revision to be able to do this job. Action must balance economic and social interests. In a number of areas the Government could take action immediately."

The Government did take immediate action. It suppressed the report. Eight years later it was finally persuaded to set up an official body to coordinate action on alcohol abuse: a Ministerial Group on Alcohol Misuse, or "Drink Tank", involving representatives from the many disparate bodies with a vested interest, including those diametrically opposing factions, the Treasury and the Department of Health & Social Security.

This seems an almost impetuously speedy example of government action on alcohol compared with the time it took to ban the Royal Navy's daily rum ration, first proposed in 1834 and finally implemented in 1968.

On the Other ... the Anti-Alcohol Lobby

The announcement of the formation of the Drink Tank in September 1987 (albeit just after the long-overdue announcement of the relaxation of our archaic licensing laws) drew a great sigh of relief from the anti-alcohol lobby, and the average British drinker might well heave a sigh of relief, too. For all of us, and journalists in particular, have been pawns in an elaborate game being played out by the anti-alcohol lobby in order to get Government to take notice of a small but serious problem. Had Government shown earlier that it might be prepared to take action on some of the problems associated with alcohol misuse, the anti-alcohol lobby would not have had to shout so loudly over the past decade to make itself heard.

It is hardly surprising that the lobbyists have sensationalized their case – most controversially by using a study of middle-aged men in the Swedish drink-smuggling port of Malmö to boost estimates of premature death caused by alcohol misuse in Britain, from the DHSS's estimate of about 4,000 in 1979 to 40,000 in 1986. They presumably felt it was necessary to overstate their case so dramatically to have it taken seriously.

And, of course, a sensational story is the best story, so reporters have seized happily on issues capable of generating headlines such as "Drinking Can Damage Your Sex Life", "Britain on the Booze" and "Drinking Ourselves to Death". The medical issues to which the scare stories relate are analysed in more dispassionate detail in Chapter Eight.

For all the twitch and flutter and inert disapproval it has induced in the drinks trade, the anti-alcohol lobby is surprisingly small and disparate. Writing in the *British Medical Journal* in 1983, its deputy editor, Dr Richard Smith, himself a campaigner committed to reducing alcohol consumption, wrote: "The power, influence, wealth, efficiency and modernity of the drink trade contrast greatly with the sad disarray of the anti-alcohol lobby."

Since then, some of the many ineffectual bodies have been wound up and much of the job transmitted to the hands of the better funded and less overtly political medical Royal Colleges – as witness the General Practitioners' 1986 report, the Psychiatrists' report *Alcohol: Our Favourite Drug* and that of the Physicians, *A Great and Growing Evil*, in 1987. They also fund "Triple A", Action on Alcohol Abuse, a small but vigorous pressure group. Alcohol Concern is a richer organization receiving Government funds, which it uses for education as well as disseminating to local councils and treatment centres. The Institute of Alcohol Studies labours under the fact that it is funded by the UK Temperance Alliance, and is behind the Action on Drinking and Driving pressure group. The Medical Council on Alcoholism tries to educate the medical profession, nurses as well as doctors, using funds donated by the drinks trade. Alcohol Forum was an attempt by Government to get out of doing anything major within its own structure by providing a forum for discussion between the Department of Health and the drinks industry. It inspired so little credibility that the chairman resigned almost as soon as he took up the appointment. The campaigners are by no means teetotal killjoys, or even very cunning, as witness their application for a drinks licence extension at a conference in October 1987.

The alcohol issue presumably played a major part in the Government's decision to close the Health Education Council, after its director, Dr David Player, had stated on a BBC2 *Brass Tacks* programme: "The alcohol industry is even more powerful in its effect on government decisions than the tobacco industry", claiming that Government had gagged the Council's campaigns against both alcohol and tobacco. The HEC has since been replaced by the much more biddable Health Education Authority.

The average British drinker has long needed more objective analysis of the medical research (most of it conducted abroad in the warmer climate of research grants) and epidemiological facts. This book is an attempt to provide them.

The Quiet Massacre

This guide is aimed at more sophisticated drinkers than those driven to violence or crime by drinking, but there is one form of alcohol-related anti-social behaviour that affects us all, whether drinkers or not: drinking and driving. It is in this area, in particular, that drinking stops being a private pleasure and becomes a public menace, where even the most determinedly libertarian drinker must feel at least a twinge of moral uncertainty.

This very special problem results from the conjunction of two elements that are each potentially dangerous. Going chain-sawing after a few drinks isn't such a good idea either, of course, but chain-sawing is a minority activity, whereas travelling by road is something most of us do several times a day. The walking drunk, even the cycling drunk, is largely (although by no means invariably) a menace to himself. The driving drunk can tragically affect the lives of many others.

In this country, at least, we still attach far too little gravity to the danger of drinking and driving, too little stigma to a fine or losing a licence. And in historical perspective it does seem odd that the problem is still so unresolved. It is hard to imagine that any other form of behaviour that regularly killed more than 1,000 people a year, many of them completely innocent victims, would still be condoned by society in general. (Just think how vigorously and expensively we campaign against the spectre of heroin use, whose annual official death toll is well under 100.) Yet we continue to press on those about to take to the wheel a drink that is terrifyingly referred to as "a nightcap" or, even more absurdly, "one for the road".

Drink is hardly new to our lives, but cars have been owned by the majority for a relatively short time. Perhaps our inexcusable insouciance comes from the fact that cars initially belonged to the rich, and casualties tended to be pedestrians who were likely to be much poorer (and therefore supposedly more expendable). There were presumably no strident media campaigns initiated by, say, the widows of farmworkers to stir up the issue in the 1930s. Then came World War II, when death was on everyone's doorstep, followed by the country's increasing prosperity and enthusiasm for a drink.

Our attitudes towards drinking and driving changed quite perceptibly, if not enough, in the years immediately after the introduction in 1967 of the Breathalyzer and a maximum legal blood-alcohol level for drivers of 80 milligrams of alcohol per 100 millilitres of blood – considerably higher than the 50mg/100ml limit in Finland, Greece, Iceland, Japan, the Netherlands, Norway, Poland, Yugoslavia and parts of Australia. (For more information on what 80mg/100ml actually means, in practical terms, see Chapter Eight, How to Handle Drink.) Probably 5,000 lives were saved and 200,000 casualties avoided in the first seven years of this much-publicized new regime. But Britain gradually learned to live with being breathalysed and convictions for drunken driving have since soared in England and Wales (while remaining fairly stable, if representing a higher proportion of the driving population, in Scotland). Convictions in England and Wales in 1984 were 101,000, more than ten times the number in 1967; Scottish convictions merely doubled to 12,213, in keeping with Britain's overall vehicle mileage.

Parliament has consistently resisted calls for random breath testing, seen by MPs, like increasing excise duties on alcoholic drinks, as a surefire vote loser. This is odd, because opinion polls show that by far the majority of ordinary British people now favour the introduction of random breath tests. The Automobile Association found in 1967 that 25 per cent were in favour of random testing and 68 per cent against. By 1975, opinion had swung firmly in favour of this form of external control: 48 per cent for and 37 per cent against. A National Opinion Poll conducted for Action on Drinking and Driving when it was formed in 1987, and whose first report was called *A Quiet Massacre*, found 77 per cent in favour of random testing, showing that the British public is now convinced that the advantages of this monitoring system and powerful social deterrent outweigh the possible disadvantages.

Random breath testing has demonstrably worked in Finland and Australia (two very different drinking cultures), yet there are still editorials in Britain suggesting that it would infringe civil liberties. The truth, of course, is that the police already have – and use – wide powers to stop drivers anyway. Surely the Englishman's right to take to the road when tight is as nought compared with the likely benefit to human life, not to mention the economic saving of a reduced accident rate. The Australians calculate that the saving to their health department is already greater than the extra cost to the police.

As a nation we are very gradually learning to kill fewer people on the roads, and it is likely that the total amount of damage wrought by drunken drivers is slowly declining, too. But unless some tighter control can be applied, we will continue to behave irresponsibly at the wheel. The opinion polls clearly show that we recognize a certain slackness in our moral fibre and are longing for someone to apply the discipline of a corset.

One of the many social improvements likely to result from our adoption of random breath testing is the copious provision of nonalcoholic drinks in social settings. This is still by no means routine, even in – or perhaps especially at – official gatherings. And it is a problem with which those in high places are concerned. In July 1987, Minister of Roads and Transport Peter Bottomley took the trouble to write to *The Spectator* pointing out the following: "Recently I watched the drinks table at the ITN reception in the Banqueting House. One quarter of the drinks were orange juice and water. They went as fast as the wine. Then each person took wine until the nonalcoholic glasses were replaced. If we as hosts allowed our guests to have a choice without having to ask, we as drivers would find it easier to avoid mixing alcohol with car keys." If journalists, given the opportunity, can show this restraint, think what the rest of the population would do.

Drinking Responsibly – Some Practical Advice

Don't Feel Guilty About Drinking

Enjoy alcohol for its unique benefits. Drinking should not be a furtive indulgence in a sin, but a celebration of enhanced social intercourse, enjoyment of some unique gastronomic experience and, for many light to moderate drinkers, a positive benefit to health.

Monitor Alcoholic Intake

Don't be guilty, but be honest. Get to know the alcohol content of anything you are likely to drink and identify the strongest (see pages 105-106). Keep a check on how much you drink every time you drink, especially if you are in a high-risk category (see page 203), if you plan to drive or to take on any other short-term responsibilities. (See also the Guide on pages 113-114.) Work out exactly how much alcohol there is in your usual drink in your usual glass. This could be an eye-opener – and a liver-saver.

Monitor Drinking Habits

Long-term monitoring of alcohol intake and patterns of drinking is just as important. The move towards dependence is usually gradual. Affirmative answers to any of the following questions would represent danger signals.

> Are you drinking more than you were a year ago?
>
> Are you losing touch with friends who don't drink as much as you do?
>
> Do you design your social life around drinking?
>
> Are you getting hangovers more frequently?
>
> Have you neglected any duties or responsibilities because of drink
> or its effects?

Drink Slowly

Savour it; alcoholic drinks are highly taxed and usually delicious liquids. Enjoy the taste. Pace yourself, with a definite total intake in mind on each occasion. Sip, and put the glass down if possible between each sip. Take every sip as a conscious act rather than adopting the cocktail-party gulp.

Don't Drink on an Empty Stomach

This is the way to maximize alcohol's intoxicating effect, and the damage it can do to the liver. When drinking (or even tasting) before a meal, try to eat or drink something, preferably high in fat or carbohydrate, a glass of milk perhaps, meanwhile or just before.

Be Wary of Neat Spirits
Undiluted spirits do maximum harm to the body, although the alcoholic strength is too high to maximize alcohol absorption and the effects of neat spirits are deceptively slow.

Be Wary of Drinks Between 15 and 30 per cent Alcohol
Drinks such as port, sherry, madeira, low-strength liqueurs such as creams, and traditional spirits diluted with only as much mixer again are absorbed fastest into the bloodstream and result in maximum intoxication.

Never Quench Thirst with an Alcoholic Drink
These potent drinks should be savoured as an adjunct to life rather than essential to it.

Don't Force Others to Drink
The thoughtful host:

> Provides something to eat with alcohol, especially with apéritifs
> Provides a non-alcoholic alternative for non-drinkers and to quench thirst
> Doesn't press drinks on others
> Doesn't insist on buying drinks in "rounds"
> Doesn't top up other people's glasses against their will
> Acknowledges that excessive drinking and driving is hazardous and discourages guests from combining them.

Feel Free Not to Drink Yourself
Encourage in yourself and others the notion of the viability of the nonalcoholic option; a soft drink or no drink is a choice just as valid as a strong drink. Never tease anyone who refuses alcohol.

Don't Drink to Escape
Drink to celebrate, drink to enhance, drink to enjoy tastes and people, but don't drink to avoid confrontations with emotional problems or fraught practical situations. This is negative rather than positive drinking.

Be Wary of Combining Alcohol With Other Drugs
Tranquillizers, sleeping pills, barbiturates, anti-convulsants and drugs for diabetics are particularly affected by alcohol and/or vice versa.

Aim for a Responsible Limit

Somewhere between 21 and 50 units a week for men and between 14 and 35 units a week for women is the upper limit of alcohol intake for health-conscious drinkers (see page 111). Above this and the risk of serious harm increases sharply. Those at special risk (see below) should consider the lower end of these limits to apply to them. Drink less but better is a useful maxim for anyone who has regularly been drinking at the upper end of these limits.

Check Whether You Are at Special Risk

Those who should be particularly wary of alcohol:

> Inexperienced drinkers
> Small people
> Women, especially when pregnant
> Women predisposed to breast cancer
> Men whose partners are trying to conceive
> Heavy smokers

Those who suffer from:

> High blood pressure
> Ulcers
> Diabetes
> Cardiomyopathy
> Gout
> Mental illness, especially depression

Those in an occupation with a particularly high rate of cirrhosis mortality:

> Anyone who sells alcoholic drink
> Anyone who works afloat
> Electrical engineers
> Restaurateurs, chefs, cooks, hotel staff
> Authors, writers, journalists

A good all-round book for those who want to cut down their drinking is *Let's drink to your health – a self-help guide to sensible drinking* by Ian Robertson and Mike Heather, published by the British Psychological Society and available at £3.95 from The Distribution Centre, Black Horse Road, Letchworth, Herts. SG6 1HN. If you think you have a drink problem, seek help immediately. The standard of help available through general practice and specialist treatment has improved enormously in recent years. There is also a national network of National Health Service alcohol problems treatment agencies and of local councils on alcoholism. These, together with Alcoholics Anonymous, Al-Anon and Al-Ateen groups, cover most of the country. Details of local facilities can be obtained from the following addresses:

England
Alcohol Concern
305 Gray's Inn Road
London WC1X 8QF
01-833 3471

Alcoholics Anonymous
UK General Services Offices
PO Box 1
Stonebow House
Stonebow
York YO1 2NJ
0904 644026
(Information about local AA groups)

Al-Anon Family Groups UK
61 Dover Street
London SE1 4YF
01-403 0888
(Information about Al-Anon groups for the families of problem drinkers. Al-Ateen, which caters for adolescent children of problem drinkers, can also be contacted at
01-403 0888)

Medical Council on Alcoholism
1 St Andrews Place
London NW1 4LB
01-487 4445
(Education for doctors and nurses)

Scotland
Scottish Council on Alcohol
137–145 Sauchiehall Street
Glasgow G2 3EW
041 333 9677
(For details of treatment agencies including local councils on alcoholism)

Northern Ireland
The Northern Ireland Council
on Alcoholism
40 Elmwood Avenue
Belfast BT9 6AZ
0232 664434
(For details of treatment agencies)

Eire
The Irish National Council
on Alcoholism
19-20 Fleet Street
Dublin 2
0001 774091
(For details of treatment agencies)

Alkana, Ronald L. and Malcolm, Richard D.,
*Hyperbaric Ethanol Antagonism in Mice: Studies on
Oxygen, Nitrogen, Strain and Sex*
Psychopharmacology 77, pp 11-16, 1982.

Armyr, Gunno, Elmer, Ake and Herz, Ulrich,
Alcohol in the World of the 80s, Sober Forlags,
Stockholm, 1982.

Barber, David, "Last NZ chance to ban
alcohol" and "The swillers and wowsers fight
on", *The Independent*, August 1987.

Baum-Baicker, Cynthia, *The Health Benefits of
Moderate Alcohol Consumption: A Review of the
Literature, Drug and Alcohol Dependence* 15,
pp 207-227, Elsevier Scientific Publishers,
Ireland, 1985.

Bauman, Larry, "Fetal Label Bill Defeated",
The Wine Spectator, Vol. XII, No. 8, 1987.

Bold, Alan (Ed), *Drink to Me Only*, Robin
Clark, 1982.

Brewers' Society *Statistical Handbook*, 1986.

British Medical Journal, Alcohol Problems, 1982.

Burke, Thomas, *English Night-Life*, Batsford,
1941.

Cancer Research Campaign, *Facts on Cancer*,
1986.

Cavanagh, John and Clairmonte, Frederick F.,
Alcoholic Beverages: Dimensions of Corporate Power,
Croom Helm, 1985.

Clare, Anthony and Adhead, Fiona, *Doctors'
double standards on alcohol*, British Medical Journal
293, pp 1590-1591, 1986.

Cornwell, Rupert, "Trouble brewing over lack
of sugar", *The Independent*, September 1987.

Crawford, Alex and Stuart, Ray, *Register of
United Kingdom Alcohol Research 1985-1986*.

Davies, Phil and Walsh, Dermot, *Alcohol
Problems and Alcohol Control in Europe*, Croom
Helm, 1983

Douglas, Mary (Ed), *Constructive Drinking*,
Cambridge University Press, 1987.

Duffy, John C. and Plant, Martin A., *Scotland's liquor licensing changes: an assessment*, British Medical Journal 292, pp 36-39, 1986.

Dunbar, James A., *A Quiet Massacre: A Review of Drinking and Driving in the United Kingdom*, The Institute of Alcohol Studies Occasional Paper 7, 1985.

Dunbar, James A., Penttila, Antti and Jarmo, Pikkarainen, *Drinking and driving: success of random breath testing in Finland*, British Medical Journal 295, pp 101-103, 1987.

Economist, "Nordic biers and evil spirits", February 3, 1987.

Economist, "The fuzzy link with cancer", May 23, 1987.

Economist, "American boozers cool it", August 29, 1987.

Economist, "Depressed spirit", September 1987.

Emerson, John, "Prepare to fight the 'growing threat' from anti-alcohol set", *Off-Licence News*, April 30, 1987.

Financial Mail (South Africa), "Rule of the few", August 14, 1987.

Ford, Gene, *Gene Ford's Moderate Drinking Journal*, Seattle, Washington.

Gossop, Michael, *Living with Drugs*, Wildwood House, 1982; 1987.

Grindal, Richard, *Exploding the Myth: The Truth About Alcohol Misuse*, The Morning Advertiser, 1987.

The Grocer, "Consumers confused by alcoholic strengths", March 14, 1987.

Gurley Brown, Helen, "Liz Taylor Survives!", *Cosmopolitan*, September 1987.

Harper, Clive, Kril, Jillian and Daly, John, *Are we drinking our neurones away?*, British Medical Journal 294, pp 534-536, 1987.

Harpers Wine and Spirit Gazette, "Education, not restrictions, urged by a responsible industry", August 21, 1987.

Harpers Wine and Spirit Gazette, "Trade to move more onto the offensive regarding the social aspects of alcohol?", September 18, 1987.

Healy, Maurice, *Stay Me With Flagons*, Michael Joseph, 1940; 1949.

Hemming, John, *Amazon Frontier*, Macmillan, 1987.

Hobhouse, Henry, *Seeds of Change*, Sidgwick & Jackson, 1985.

Hughes, Robert, *The Fatal Shore*, Collins Harvill, 1987.

Hyams, Edward, *Dionysus: A Social History of the Wine Vine*, Thames & Hudson, 1965; Sidgwick & Jackson, 1987.

Inglis, Brian, *The Forbidden Game*, Hodder & Stoughton, 1985.

Kendell, R. E., *Drinking Sensibly*, transcript of the First Benno Pollak Lécture, Institute of Psychiatry, London, 1987.

Kenyon, Roger and Howa, Nazeem, *South Africa's Harvest of Shame*, Reader's Digest, September 1986.

Kinney, Jean and Leaton, Gwen, *Understanding Alcohol*, Mosby Medical Library, St. Louis, Missouri, 1982.

Kohn, Marek, *Narcomania*, Faber and Faber, 1987.

Latcham, Richard W., Kreitman, Norman, Plant, Martin A. and Crawford, Alex, *Regional variation in British alcohol morbidity rates: a myth uncovered?* I: Clinical surveys, II: Population surveys, British Medical Journal 289, pp 1341-1345, 1984.

Lister, Richard G. and Nutt, David J., "Is R015-4513 a specific alcohol antagonist?" *Trends in neurosciences*, June 1987.

McDonald, Janet T., *Wine and Nutrition*, A Smyposium on Wine, Health and Society, California Wine Institute, 1986.

McGee, Harold, *On Food and Cooking*, Charles Scribner's, 1984.

MacSween, Roderick N. M., *Alcohol and Cancer*, British Medical Bulletin 38, No. 1, pp 31-33, 1982.

Mintel, *Changing Lifestyles in the Alcoholic Drinks Market*, 1987.

Morgan, Marsha Y., *Sex and Alcohol*, British Medical Bulletin 38, No. 1, pp 43-52, 1982.

Morrice, Philip, *The Schweppes Guide to Scotch*, Alphabooks, 1983.

Muir Gray, J. A., "Therapy of the Pub", *Brewing Review 1978*, pp 2-4.

New Scientist, "The spirit is lucid, but the flesh is drunk", December 11, 1986.

O'Brien, Robert and Chafetz, Morris (Eds), *The Encyclopedia of Alcoholism*, Green Spring, USA, 1982.

Peck, David F. and Plant, Martin A., *Unemployment and illegal drug use; concordant evidence from a prospective study and national trends*, British Medical Journal 293, pp 929-932, 1986.

Plant, Martin A. (Ed), *Drinking and Problem Drinking*, Junction Books, 1982.

Plant, Martin A., *Drugs in Perspective*, Hodder & Stoughton, 1981; 1987.

Plant, Martin A. and Moira L., "Alcohol and Alcohol Problems Research, Scotland", *British Journal of Addiction*, pp 17-21, 1986.

Plant, Moira L., *Alcohol and Pregnancy*, World Health Organization, Division of Mental Health Fact Sheet, 1987.

Plant, Moira L., *Drinking and Pregnancy*, International Clinical Nutrition Review, 1988.

Plant, Moira L., *Women and Alcohol, Women's Problems in General Practice*, Oxford University Press, 1987.

Plant, Moira L., *Women, Drinking and Pregnancy*, Tavistock, 1985.

Platter, John, "Opinion", *Wine Times*, South Africa, August, 1987.

Robertson, Ian and Heather, Nick, *So you want to cut down your drinking?*, Scottish Health Education Group, Edinburgh.

Roman, E., et al, *Pregnancy and Drinking*, Teratology, 1987.

Royal College of General Practitioners, *Alcohol – A Balanced View*, 1986.

Royal College of Physicians, *A Great and Growing Evil*, Tavistock, 1987.

Royal College of Psychiatrists, *Alcohol: Our Favourite Drug*, Tavistock, 1986.

Sainsbury's, *Living Today, No. 5, Sensible Drinking*, 1987.

Schaerf, Wilfred, "Wine farms remain hooked on dop system", *Cape Times*, May 11, 1987.

Simon, André L., *The History of the Wine Trade in England*, Vols. I, II and III, Holland Press, 1964.

The Spectator, "Driven to Drink", August 29, 1987.

Timbs, Olivia, "Calculating the risks of breast cancer", *The Independent*, May, 1987.

Waugh, Auberon, "The bolshie bishop fights the bottle", *The Spectator*, April 4, 1987.

Whitaker, Ben, *The Global Connection – The Crisis of Drug Addiction*, Jonathan Cape, 1987; Methuen London, 1988.

Wilson, C. Anne, *Food and Drink in Britain*, Constable, 1973.

Graphs
Page 131: Spring J.A. and Buss D.H. (1977) Three centuries of alcohol in the British Diet. *Nature* 270, 567–72. Brewers' Society *Statistical Handbook*, 1986. Pages 147–8: Brewers' Society *Statistical Handbook*, 1986. World Health Organization 1984, 1985. Page 188: Office of Population Censuses and Surveys (Personal Communication) (1986).

INDEX

When a subject is referred to a number of times throughout the book, a main entry is indicated in **bold**.

Janet W. Macdonald

The Super Saleswoman

'When the stakes are high, the competition legion and the customers limited, there is only one rule that matters – if you've got an edge, use it. As a woman, you have that edge anyway. This book is to help you sharpen it.'

Good salespeople are the lifeblood of any business and are rewarded by their employers in ways that reflect their importance. Not only are the top salespeople in any organisation likely to be among the highest paid, they are given prizes and praise is heaped upon them. In big companies, pride of place at the annual convention goes to the best sales team, and more and more frequently these days, that top team is dominated by women.

In many selling situations, a woman can gain an appointment where a man cannot, and once in front of the customer can use her innate skills in handling people to win an order. With this in mind, many selling organisations are actively recruiting women.

The purpose of this book is to show those women who want to get into selling how and where to start as well as develop their sales careers; and to show those who are already selling how to improve their techniques and lift themselves into the 'high flier' category.

It covers everything from cold prospecting to closing the sale: including how to dress for your market; how to manage your time; how to conduct a formal presentation; how to deal with difficult customers, colleagues and family; how to cope with domestic and social commitments; and how to move up into sales management – and it does it all from the woman's viewpoint.

Janet W. Macdonald

Climbing The Ladder

'Nice girls don't compete, they sit politely and wait to be chosen. Generations of women have grown up convinced that if they do their best, they will be noticed and rewarded, then wondered why the rewards were not forthcoming.'

Since the early 1970s the number of women gaining high-level posts and high-level salaries has been steadily increasing, but progress is still very slow. There is no logical or physiological reason why a woman should not run a major international company, but there are a number of psychological reasons why few succeed in doing so.

Three main enemies must be fought if women want their share of opportunity: the company – its history, structure and attitudes; men – both in the office and in private life; and themselves – their self-respect, self-image, self-confidence, their vision of what they want from life and their desire and determination to attain it. And many women are their own worst enemies.

This book will enable all women to recognise and defeat these enemies by drawing up a battle-plan to give the basics of career planning, time management, home life management and the management of relationships with superiors, peers and staff. It may be harder for women to climb the corporate ladder than for men, but once they have put into practice the sound advice in this book, they will find that the view from the top far outweighs the effort of climbing.

Janet Macdonald is an accountant by profession, and is currently a manager in an international banking group.

Roger Cook
Tim Tate

What's Wrong With Your Rights?

Did you know that:

— an Englishman's home is *not* his castle – dozens of people have the right to enter your home without permission?
— by the end of the century a policeman on the beat will have instant access to all your medical, social services, criminal and financial records at the touch of a computer button?
— an unmarried father has no legal rights to his child?
— we have no statutory right to freedom of speech?

This book reveals the *real* situation regarding your rights. Roger Cook and Tim Tate, from Central Television's investigative series *The Cook Report*, dissect our legal system to show how our traditional 'rights' – if they ever existed – are constantly being eroded or threatened.

Drawing on a wealth of case histories and personal tragedies, *What's Wrong With Your Rights?* is a searing indictment of the way government, local councils, the law and big business can legally ride roughshod over the ordinary citizen who pays for their very existence. It is a compelling warning of the dangers of complacency as we go about our daily lives.

'An excellent compendium of oppression'
Literary Review

'A grim case-study of how fragile our rights are'
Sunday Express

Nicholas Coleridge

The Fashion Conspiracy

From the catwalks of Paris to the sweatshops of South Korea; from Seventh Avenue glitz to Tokyo new-wave ... The sophisticated brokings of the fashion conspiracy have generated a powerful new force in the world economy; designer money.

Nicholas Coleridge presents a fascinating portrait of the jet-setting matrons who are the gurus and tyrants of the fashion press; of fashion legends like Paloma Pícasso and Tina Chow; of the top store buyers who command $700 million a season. He probes the incredible world of the designer billionaires like Ralph Lauren, Calvin Klein and Yves St Laurent whose fashion empires are richer than entire Third World countries.

Here are the jealousies, the glamour, the buccaneering, the espionage and the razzmatazz in a witty and penetrating guide to an extraordinary world.

'Nicholas Coleridge returns as an explorer from where the wild things are; the largely untravelled zones of fashion. His account is incisive, entertaining and alarming. It is this book's novelistic qualities that so distinguish it; the scene-setting, the dialogue, the groupings of characters, the clashes of huge temperaments, the moments of high drama.'

The Times

'Wickedly funny, vivid visual sketches, sharp observations. Coleridge sketches, with lines as spare a Cocteau's, the characters from fashion's high life.'

Independent

Mihir Bose

The Crash

- Controversial and hard-hitting analysis of the crash
- Why it happened, what happened and what it means
- Its implications for future worldwide financial stability

In the early part of October 1987 the world's stock markets were at record levels. By the end of the month they were in disarray with record falls not only in London and New York but also in Tokyo, Sydney and Hong Kong, where trading was suspended.

This forthright critique of the whole system is an intricately detailed account of the prelude to and the aftermath of the collapse in which thousands of people in the market lost their jobs; a sobering indictment of the powers who foresaw the situation but chose to disregard it; and a prescription for avoiding the next crash.

With its lucid and jargonless prose, *The Crash* is required reading for all potential investors, shareholders – especially the growing army of new and small shareholders – financial experts and anyone interested in how the market works.

Financial journalist Mihir Bose was Deputy Editor of *Financial Weekly* and City Features Editor of the *London Daily News*. He now writes for several national newspapers.

'Rich in colourful detail ... a vivid picture of how the impact of Black Monday and Terrible Tuesday rippled around the world.'

Financial Times

'Exhilarating reading ... a worthwhile read ... an instant eye-opener.'

Time Out

Vernon Coleman

The Health Scandal

The sickest thing about Britain today is its health services

- through a mixture of incompetence and dishonesty the NHS wastes several billion pounds every year
- some consultants deliberately keep their NHS waiting lists long as a means of acquiring private patients
- many surgeons choose to do spectacular high-tech operations rather than reducing queues for hip-joint replacements and hernia operations
- some fashionable 'alternative' medicine philosophies are potentially highly dangerous
- stress-related illness costs British industry around £20,000 million each year, and more people than ever are dissatisfied with the health care they receive

Although we may live longer than before as a nation, we are getting steadily sicker despite advances in modern medicine, and misjudged 'breakthroughs' are likely to bring about a situation in thirty years where a small, healthy, working population is forced to support a large, diseased, geriatric one. Private medicine, the NHS, drug companies, GPs, local authorities, hospitals, alternative practitioners, and virtually everybody concerned with the nation's health comes under critical scrutiny in this controversial book, for Vernon Coleman argues that everywhere there is wastage, incompetence, ignorance and, all too frequently, the direst of consequences – a decline in patients' health.

This book will astonish, depress, confound and upset many of its readers but, however disagreeable the diagnosis may be, it had better be taken seriously – for the sake of the nation's health.

'It is not necessary to accept his conclusion to be able to savour his decidedly trenchant comments on today's medicine . . . a book to stimulate and to make one argue.

British Medical Journal

David Leigh

The Wilson Plot

Was a British Prime Minister hounded out of office by bogus elements inside MI5 and the CIA who sought to discredit him as a Soviet agent?

It could be the lurid plot of a bestselling thriller . . . Yet in *The Wilson Plot* leading investigative journalist David Leigh reveals the full true story behind the extraordinary conspiracy first hinted at by Peter Wright. Drawing on Wright's own private confessions and unpublished correspondence, on the recollections of MI5 and MI6 officers, and on the testimony of former FBI and CIA members, Leigh explores how Wright himself and CIA chief James Angleton led a bizarre campaign against Labour Prime Minister Harold Wilson, his government advisers and friends.

In his history of recklessly – even treasonably – uncontrolled intelligence service activity Leigh reveals among much else:

● how 10 Downing Street was being bugged by secret department 'K5' just prior to Wilson's resignation in 1976
● how Wright had tried to persuade a group of colleagues to go *en masse* to Wilson and frighten him into secretly standing down
● how allegations regarding Wilson's private life were secretly and routinely circulated by MI5 to the press and to Conservative MPs
● how Wright was obsessed with the activities of Wilson's friend and raincoat manufacturer Lord Kagan – at a time when the existence of real traitors such as Anthony Blunt was being assiduously hushed up

Grotesquely fascinating in its convolutions and terrifying in its import, the history of *The Wilson Plot* is the most controversial book since *Spycatcher*.

A Selected List of Non-Fiction Available from Mandarin Books

While every effort is made to keep prices low, it is sometimes necessary to increase prices at short notice. Mandarin Paperbacks reserves the right to show new retail prices on covers which may differ from those previously advertised in the text or elsewhere.

The prices shown below were correct at the time of going to press.

All these books are available at your bookshop or newsagent, or can be ordered direct from the publisher. Just tick the titles you want and fill in the form below.

Mandarin Paperbacks, Cash Sales Department, PO Box 11, Falmouth, Cornwall TR10 9EN.

Please send cheque or postal order, no currency, for purchase price quoted and allow the following for postage and packing:

UK   55p for the first book, 22p for the second book and 14p for each additional book ordered to a maximum charge of £1.75.

BFPO and Eire   55p for the first book, 22p for the second book and 14p for each of the next seven books, thereafter 8p per book.

Overseas Customers   £1.00 for the first book plus 25p per copy for each additional book.

NAME (Block Letters) ....

ADDRESS ....

....